LIFE

FIELD MANUAL

WHAT THEY DIDN'T TELL

YOU:

Life after turning 50!

Kevin B DiBacco

Table of Contents

About the author

Kevin's journey in the world of fitness and resilience is nothing short of extraordinary. At the young age of 22, Kevin ventured into the realm of powerlifting, a pursuit that would define his life for the next four decades. However, this journey was far from smooth, as he encountered numerous injuries and had to undergo multiple surgeries along the way. In fact, Kevin's friends and family playfully quip that he has spent more time in the operating room than many newly minted orthopedic surgeons. While a humorous remark, it bears a kernel of truth.

Kevin's medical history is a testament to his unwavering determination. He has endured six knee operations, undergone two major back surgeries, received two hip replacements, and even faced the challenges of brain surgery and brain radiation. It's no wonder that he has earned the moniker "Life Warrior" for his indomitable spirit and relentless pursuit of a healthier, more vibrant life.

As the years rolled on, Kevin's passion for fitness never waned. At the age of 62, he embarked on a remarkable journey to shed 60 pounds, defying the notion that age is a barrier to transformation. This determination and resilience characterized his entire life.

Kevin's accomplishments in powerlifting are a testament to his strength and dedication. During the 1990s, he achieved an unofficial bench press record of a staggering 515 pounds while maintaining a body weight of 235 pounds. Beyond powerlifting, he dabbled in a variety of sports, including baseball, softball, football, and even tried out for minor league baseball and semi-pro football teams.

One of Kevin's defining traits is his ability to rebound from adversity. Regardless of how many times life has knocked him down, he has consistently found innovative ways to reinvent himself and emerge stronger than before.

In response to his own challenges and experiences, Kevin developed "ISO QUICK STRENGTH," a program designed to help individuals get back on their feet as swiftly as possible. But it's not just about physical recovery; Kevin recognized the critical importance of the mind-body connection in overcoming difficult times.

His efforts to assist others extend beyond fitness programs. Kevin has shared his wisdom and insights through a blog and authored books aimed at helping people rise above adversity. His overarching message is clear: "Those who quit will always fail." This simple yet profound mantra encapsulates the essence of Kevin's life journey—a journey marked by resilience, determination, and a relentless pursuit of personal growth and well-being. After a remarkable 37-year career as a filmmaker and video producer, Kevin now wields the mighty pen to craft captivating stories in the form of books.

Chapter 1: The Preconceptions of Turning 50

The Milestone Birthday

Turning 50 is a milestone that many people approach with a mix of excitement and trepidation. It is a time when one transitions from middle age to a new chapter of life, and it often comes with a range of emotions and reflections. In this subchapter, we will explore what turning 50 truly means and shed light on what they don't tell you about this significant milestone.

As you reach the age of 50, you may find yourself contemplating what you have accomplished so far and what lies ahead. It is a time for self-reflection, a chance to reassess your goals and dreams. But what they don't tell you is that turning 50 is not the end; it's just the beginning of a new and exciting phase of life.

One aspect that surprises many is the sense of liberation that comes with turning 50. You start to care less about what others think and become more comfortable in your own skin. This newfound confidence allows you to pursue your passions and take on new challenges without fear of judgment.

Another truth about turning 50 is the importance of self-care. You may have spent the previous decades prioritizing others, whether it was raising a family or building a career. But now is the time to focus on yourself. It's okay to put your needs first and make choices that contribute to your well-being and happiness.

One aspect that is often overlooked when discussing turning 50 is the opportunity for personal growth. It's never too late to learn something new or embark on a new adventure. This chapter of life offers a chance to reinvent yourself, to explore new interests, and to embrace change.

However, it's crucial to acknowledge that turning 50 also comes with some challenges. Physical changes, such as menopause or age-related health issues, may arise. But what they don't tell you is that these challenges can be overcome with the right mindset and a proactive approach to your health.

In conclusion, turning 50 is a milestone birthday that brings a mix of emotions and reflections. It's a time of self-discovery, personal growth, and renewed confidence. While there may be challenges along the way, they can be overcome with the right attitude and a focus on self-care. Embrace this milestone with open arms and look forward to the exciting possibilities that lie ahead.

Society's Expectations and Stereotypes

As we approach the milestone of turning 50, it becomes evident that society holds certain expectations and stereotypes about this stage of life. These societal pressures can often create unnecessary stress and anxiety, making it crucial to recognize and challenge these preconceived notions. In this subchapter, we will delve into society's expectations and stereotypes surrounding turning 50, shedding light on the truth behind them.

One of the most common stereotypes associated with turning 50 is the midlife crisis. Many believe that once we reach this age, we are destined to experience a sudden urge to make drastic changes in our lives. While it is true that some individuals may go through a period of self-reflection and reevaluation during this time, it is important to remember that not everyone will experience a midlife crisis. Each person's journey is unique, and it is essential to embrace the diversity of experiences that come with turning 50.

Additionally, society often places significant emphasis on physical appearance and youthfulness. We are bombarded with images of youthful vitality and the notion that aging is something to be feared or hidden. However, the truth is that turning 50 brings wisdom, resilience, and a newfound sense of self-acceptance. It is a time to celebrate the accomplishments and experiences that have shaped us, rather than focusing solely on outward appearances.

Another expectation society often imposes on those turning 50 is the notion that it is a time to slow down and retire from active engagement in life. While some individuals may choose to transition into a more relaxed lifestyle, others may find themselves embarking on new adventures and pursuing long-held dreams. The possibilities are endless at this stage of life, and it is essential to challenge the notion that turning 50 means slowing down.

In conclusion, society's expectations and stereotypes surrounding turning 50 can often be misleading and limiting. It is crucial to recognize that each individual's journey is unique and to challenge these preconceived notions. Turning 50 is a time of self-discovery, growth, and embracing the wisdom that comes with age. By breaking free from societal pressures, we can truly embrace the truth about turning 50 and create a vibrant and fulfilling life that defies stereotypes.

Emotional Rollercoaster: Dealing with Mixed Feelings

Turning 50 is a major milestone in life. It's a time when you reflect on your achievements, evaluate your goals, and perhaps even experience a whirlwind of emotions. This subchapter explores the emotional rollercoaster that many individuals face when they reach this significant age, shedding light on the mixed feelings that often accompany this transition.

One of the first emotions that may arise when turning 50 is a sense of nostalgia. Memories of the past flood your mind, reminding you of all the experiences, relationships, and adventures you've had. It's common to feel a strong attachment to these memories and even a longing to relive certain moments. However, it's important to remember that turning 50 is not about dwelling in the past but rather embracing the present and looking forward to the future.

Mixed with nostalgia, many individuals also experience a sense of excitement as they enter this new phase of life. It's a time when you have the opportunity to reinvent yourself, try new things, and pursue long-held dreams. The prospect of embarking on new adventures and exploring uncharted territories can be invigorating and exhilarating.

However, alongside these positive emotions, turning 50 can also bring about feelings of anxiety and uncertainty. Questions about health, retirement, and the overall direction of your life may start to creep in. It's completely normal to feel apprehensive about the unknown, but it's essential to remember that you have the power to shape your own destiny and make the most of this chapter.

Moreover, turning 50 often brings a heightened awareness of mortality. The realization that time is passing quickly can be both sobering and overwhelming. It's natural to reflect on the legacy you want to leave behind and the impact you've made on the world. This realization can serve as a catalyst for personal growth and motivate you to live each day to the fullest.

In conclusion, turning 50 is a time of mixed emotions. Nostalgia, excitement, anxiety, and a heightened awareness of mortality all play a role in this emotional rollercoaster. It's crucial to acknowledge and embrace these feelings, as they are an integral part of the transition into this new phase of life. By recognizing and understanding these emotions, you can navigate the emotional rollercoaster with grace and make the most of this exciting chapter.

The Fear of Aging and Mortality

As we approach the milestone of turning 50, it is quite common to experience a range of emotions. One of the most prevalent and often unspoken fears is the fear of aging and mortality. This chapter aims to address this fear head-on and provide insights and perspectives to help you navigate this stage of life with grace and acceptance.

It is natural for everyone to have concerns about aging and mortality. The realization that our bodies are changing and that time is passing by can be unsettling. Thoughts about our own mortality may start to creep in, leaving us feeling anxious and uncertain about the future. However, it is essential to remember that turning 50 is not the end but merely the beginning of a new chapter in life.

One of the keys to overcoming the fear of aging is to change our perspective. Instead of focusing on the negative aspects, we can choose to embrace the wisdom and experiences that come with age. Turning 50 brings a sense of liberation and self-acceptance, allowing us to let go of societal expectations and embrace who we truly are.

Moreover, it is important to recognize that aging is a natural part of life. We cannot control the passage of time, but we can control how we approach it. By taking care of our physical and mental well-being, we can age gracefully and maintain a positive outlook on life. Engaging in regular exercise, eating a balanced diet, and nurturing meaningful relationships are all crucial elements of healthy aging.

Additionally, it is essential to address any underlying fears or anxieties about mortality. Reflecting on our lives and acknowledging our accomplishments can help us find meaning and purpose in the present moment. Connecting with others who share similar concerns can provide a sense of community and support, reminding us that we are not alone in this journey.

In conclusion, the fear of aging and mortality is a common sentiment that many individuals experience as they approach the milestone of turning 50. However, by shifting our perspective, taking care of our physical and mental well-being, and finding meaning and purpose in our lives, we can overcome this fear and embrace this new chapter with open arms. Remember, turning 50 is an opportunity for growth, self-discovery, and a celebration of the life we have lived thus far.

Chapter 2: Physical Changes and Health Considerations

The Impact of Hormonal Shifts

When it comes to turning 50, there are numerous changes that occur within our bodies. One of the most significant changes is the hormonal shifts that take place. These shifts can have a profound impact on our physical, emotional, and mental well-being. In this subchapter, we will explore the truth about hormonal shifts and what they don't tell you.

For both men and women, the hormonal changes that occur in their 50s can be quite dramatic. Women experience menopause during this time, which marks the end of their reproductive years. The decrease in estrogen and progesterone levels can lead to hot flashes, night sweats, mood swings, and vaginal dryness. Additionally, hormonal shifts can also increase the risk of osteoporosis and heart disease in women.

Men, on the other hand, go through andropause, also known as male menopause. This is a gradual decline in testosterone levels, which can result in decreased libido, fatigue, weight gain, and even depression. Many men are unaware of the impact that hormonal shifts can have on their overall well-being and often attribute these changes to the natural aging process.

It is important for everyone to understand that these hormonal shifts are a normal part of the aging process. However, they can significantly affect our quality of life if left unaddressed. By recognizing and acknowledging the impact of hormonal shifts, we can take proactive steps to manage and minimize their effects.

There are various treatment options available to help alleviate the symptoms associated with hormonal shifts. Hormone replacement therapy (HRT) is one such option that can be beneficial for both men and women. HRT involves replacing the hormones that are no longer being produced in adequate amounts, thereby restoring balance and reducing symptoms.

In addition to medical interventions, lifestyle changes can also play a crucial role in managing hormonal shifts. Regular exercise, a healthy diet, and stress reduction techniques can help alleviate symptoms and promote overall well-being. It is essential to prioritize self-care during this time and listen to your body's needs.

In conclusion, the impact of hormonal shifts cannot be underestimated when it comes to turning 50. Whether you are a man or a woman, understanding these changes and seeking appropriate treatment and lifestyle adjustments can make a world of difference in your overall quality of life. By addressing hormonal shifts head-on, you can navigate this stage of life with grace and confidence. Remember, turning 50 is just another chapter in our journey, and with the right knowledge and support, it can be a fulfilling and empowering one.

Body Changes: What to Expect

As we approach the milestone of turning 50, it is crucial to be prepared for the various changes that our bodies will inevitably experience. While many books and articles focus on the emotional and psychological aspects of this phase of life, it is equally important to understand the physical transformations that occur. In this subchapter, we will explore the body changes that you can expect as you reach the age of 50, shedding light on what they don't tell you.

One of the most notable changes that many individuals experience is a decrease in metabolism. As we age, our bodies naturally slow down, leading to weight gain and a higher likelihood of developing health conditions such as diabetes or high blood pressure. It becomes essential to adopt a healthier lifestyle by incorporating regular exercise and a balanced diet to maintain overall well-being.

Another significant change is the loss of muscle mass and bone density. This can result in decreased strength and flexibility, making everyday activities more challenging. Engaging in strength training exercises and consuming foods rich in calcium and vitamin D can help counteract these effects, ensuring that you maintain bone health and muscle strength.

Hormonal changes are also prevalent during this stage of life, particularly in women. Menopause, characterized by the cessation of menstruation, can bring about a plethora of symptoms such as hot flashes, mood swings, and sleep disturbances. Understanding these changes and seeking appropriate medical advice can help manage these symptoms effectively, ensuring a smoother transition into this new phase of life.

It is important to note that everyone's experience with turning 50 will be unique. While some individuals may encounter these changes more prominently, others may not experience them at all. Nonetheless, having a basic understanding of what to expect allows us to be better prepared both physically and mentally.

In conclusion, turning 50 is a significant milestone that brings about various changes in our bodies. By being aware of what to expect, we can take proactive steps to maintain our overall health and well-being. Remember, this is just one chapter of your life, and with the right mindset and knowledge, you can embrace this new phase with grace and vitality.

Health Screenings and Preventative Measures

Taking care of your health becomes increasingly important as you approach the milestone of turning 50. While aging is a natural process, it is essential to stay on top of your health and be proactive in preventing potential health issues. In this subchapter, we will explore the significance of health screenings and the preventative measures you can take to maintain your well-being.

Regular health screenings are crucial in detecting potential health concerns early on. As you age, your risk of developing certain conditions such as heart disease, diabetes, and certain types of cancer increases. By undergoing screenings, you can identify any underlying issues before they progress, allowing for more effective treatment options.

One of the most important screenings for individuals over 50 is a comprehensive annual physical examination. This includes checks for blood pressure, cholesterol levels, and blood glucose levels. These tests can uncover early signs of heart disease, diabetes, and other chronic conditions.

Additionally, certain cancers become more prevalent with age, making screenings for breast, colorectal, and prostate cancers imperative. Regular mammograms, colonoscopies, and prostate-specific antigen (PSA) tests can detect abnormalities or cancerous growths that may require further investigation or treatment.

Furthermore, preventive measures play a vital role in maintaining your overall health. Engaging in regular physical activity, such as walking, swimming, or yoga, can help prevent chronic diseases, improve cardiovascular health, and boost your immune system. Aim for at least 150 minutes of moderate-intensity exercise per week.

A well-balanced diet is equally important in preventing age-related health issues. Incorporate plenty of fruits, vegetables, whole grains, and lean proteins into your meals while limiting your intake of saturated fats, sugars, and processed foods. Stay hydrated by drinking an adequate amount of water throughout the day.

Don't forget the importance of mental and emotional well-being. Engage in activities that promote relaxation and stress reduction, such as meditation, deep breathing exercises, or pursuing hobbies you enjoy. Surround yourself with positive relationships and seek support when needed.

Remember, turning 50 is not a time to neglect your health. By staying proactive and embracing regular health screenings, adopting preventative measures, and prioritizing your overall well-being, you can enjoy a fulfilling and healthy life well beyond this milestone. Embrace this chapter of your life with the knowledge and empowerment to take control of your health and live your best life yet.

Navigating Menopause or Andropause

Menopause and andropause – two terms that often bring a mix of confusion, fear, and curiosity. As we approach the age of 50, these natural biological processes begin to unfold, bringing about significant changes in our bodies and lifestyles. In this subchapter, we will shed light on the truth about menopause and andropause, providing valuable insights and guidance for both men and women.

For women, menopause marks the end of their reproductive years, resulting in a range of physical and emotional symptoms. Hot flashes, night sweats, mood swings, and sleep disturbances are just a few of the many challenges women face during this time. However, it's important to remember that menopause is not a disease or an end, but rather a new beginning. By understanding the hormonal changes occurring in the body, women can better navigate this transition. We will explore various coping strategies, including lifestyle changes, hormone replacement therapy, and alternative remedies that can help alleviate symptoms and improve overall well-being.

On the other hand, andropause refers to the age-related decline in testosterone levels in men. Although less commonly discussed, andropause can have a profound impact on men's physical and emotional health. Symptoms such as fatigue, reduced libido, weight gain, and mood swings can be challenging to navigate. However, by recognizing the signs and seeking appropriate medical advice, men can regain their vitality and maintain a fulfilling life. We will delve into the available treatment options, including hormone replacement therapy, lifestyle changes, and natural supplements that can support men in managing andropause effectively.

Furthermore, we will explore the common misconceptions and societal stigmas surrounding menopause and andropause. By debunking myths and shedding light on the realities of these stages of life, we aim to empower individuals to embrace and celebrate this new chapter. We will also emphasize the importance of open communication and support networks, as sharing experiences and seeking guidance from peers and healthcare professionals can greatly alleviate the challenges associated with menopause and andropause.

Whether you are a woman approaching menopause or a man experiencing the symptoms of andropause, this subchapter is a valuable resource for understanding and navigating these transformative stages. By dispelling myths, providing strategies, and fostering a supportive community, we aim to equip readers with the knowledge and tools necessary to embrace the truth about turning 50 and beyond. Remember, menopause and andropause are not endings, but rather opportunities for growth, self-discovery, and a renewed sense of well-being.

Chapter 3: Relationships and Social Dynamics

Rediscovering Identity and Purpose

Turning 50 is often seen as a milestone in one's life. It is a time when we reflect on our achievements, assess our goals, and contemplate our purpose. However, what they don't tell you is that this phase of life can also be overwhelming and confusing. It is during this time that we may find ourselves questioning our identity and purpose, wondering if we have truly lived up to our potential.

Rediscovering our identity and purpose is a journey that everyone, regardless of age, can relate to. It is a process of self-discovery, where we delve into the depths of our being to understand who we truly are and what brings us fulfillment. The truth about turning 50 is that it provides an opportunity for us to redefine ourselves and find a renewed sense of purpose.

One of the first steps in this journey is to pause and reflect on our past accomplishments and experiences. Take the time to acknowledge and appreciate all that you have achieved so far. Celebrate the milestones and learn from the challenges. This reflection will help you gain insights into your strengths, values, and passions.

As we age, our priorities may shift, and our interests may change. Embrace this evolution and allow yourself to explore new avenues and passions. Rediscovering your purpose may involve stepping out of your comfort zone and trying new things. It could be pursuing a long-lost hobby, volunteering for a cause close to your heart, or even embarking on a new career path. The possibilities are endless.

Rediscovering your identity also involves reconnecting with your true self. This can be done through self-care practices such as mindfulness, meditation, and journaling. Take the time to listen to your inner voice and follow your intuition. Embrace the wisdom that comes with age and trust yourself to make the right decisions.

Finally, remember that this journey is not a solo endeavor. Surround yourself with a supportive network of family and friends who uplift and inspire you. Engage in meaningful conversations and share your aspirations with those who believe in you. Collaborate with like-minded individuals who share your passions and can help you grow.

In conclusion, turning 50 is an opportunity to rediscover our identity and purpose. It is a time to reflect, explore, and embrace our true selves. By celebrating our achievements, embracing new experiences, and nurturing our relationships, we can embark on a fulfilling journey of self-discovery. So, embrace this new chapter of life and let it be a catalyst for personal growth and transformation.

Parenting Adult Children: Support or Letting Go?

As we reach the milestone of turning 50, we find ourselves facing a whole new set of challenges, one of which is navigating the complex role of parenting adult children. This stage of life often brings with it a mix of emotions and uncertainties as we strive to strike the right balance between supporting our children and allowing them to find their own path.

It is natural for parents to want to protect and guide their children, regardless of their age. However, as our children grow into adults, it becomes crucial to reassess our role and redefine our boundaries. This subchapter explores the question that plagues many parents: should we continue to support our adult children or let go?

Supporting our adult children has its merits. We have a wealth of experience and wisdom that we can share with them. Our support can be invaluable as they navigate the challenges of career choices, relationships, and financial decisions. By offering guidance and being a sounding board, we can help them make informed choices and avoid potential pitfalls.

On the other hand, there comes a point where we must let go and allow our adult children to make their own mistakes and learn from them. It is essential for their personal growth and independence. By stepping back, we empower them to take responsibility for their own lives and develop the necessary skills to navigate the world on their own.

Finding the right balance between support and letting go requires open communication and mutual respect. It is crucial to establish clear expectations and boundaries with our adult children, ensuring that they understand our role as parents and their responsibility as independent individuals. This subchapter provides practical tips and advice on how to foster a healthy relationship with adult children, including setting boundaries, offering support without enabling, and cultivating open and honest communication.

Ultimately, the decision to support or let go depends on the unique circumstances and dynamics of each family. There is no one-size-fits-all approach. However, by exploring this topic, we aim to provide insights and guidance that can help parents navigate this challenging stage of life.

Whether you are a parent on the cusp of turning 50 or someone interested in understanding the complexities of parenting adult children, this subchapter offers valuable perspectives and practical advice. By recognizing that our adult children need both our support and space to grow, we can ensure that we strike the right balance and foster healthy relationships as we journey through this exciting phase of life.

Maintaining Healthy Friendships and Social Circles

As we navigate the journey of life, one thing becomes abundantly clear - the importance of healthy friendships and social circles. Turning 50 is a milestone that often brings about significant changes in our lives, and it's crucial to understand how to maintain and nurture these vital connections during this transformative phase. In this subchapter, we will delve into the truth about maintaining healthy friendships and social circles, uncovering what they don't tell you about turning 50.

At 50, many individuals find themselves facing new challenges and transitions such as empty nests, career changes, or even retirement. These changes can sometimes lead to feelings of isolation or loneliness if not adequately addressed. However, by actively seeking ways to maintain and develop healthy friendships and social circles, you can enhance your overall well-being and find support during these times of change.

One essential aspect of maintaining healthy friendships is communication. As we age, our priorities and interests may shift, and it's crucial to openly communicate these changes with our friends. By expressing our needs, desires, and limitations, we can ensure that our friendships continue to evolve and grow alongside us. This subchapter will provide practical tips on effective communication techniques to deepen connections with friends and foster understanding.

Another often overlooked aspect of maintaining healthy friendships is self-care. Turning 50 is a time when we must prioritize our own well-being, both physically and mentally. By taking care of ourselves, we can show up as our best selves in our friendships and social circles. From setting boundaries to engaging in activities that bring us joy, this subchapter will explore various self-care practices that can positively impact our relationships.

Additionally, this subchapter will shed light on the importance of diversifying our social circles. While our long-term friendships hold significant value, it's equally important to expand our networks and embrace new connections. By actively seeking out new friendships and engaging in community activities, we open ourselves up to diverse perspectives and experiences, enriching our lives in unimaginable ways.

Turning 50 is an opportunity to reevaluate and strengthen our relationships. By focusing on maintaining healthy friendships and social circles, we can navigate this transformative phase with grace and fulfillment. This subchapter will provide practical advice, personal anecdotes, and expert insights to guide you in cultivating the connections that will support and uplift you throughout your journey.

Remember, it's never too late to invest in your friendships and social circles. Start today, and you'll discover the immense joy and fulfillment that come from maintaining healthy relationships at any age.

Romantic Relationships: Challenges and Opportunities

When it comes to turning 50, one aspect of life that often takes center stage is romantic relationships. This is a time when many individuals find themselves reflecting on their past experiences and contemplating what the future holds for their love life. In this subchapter, we will explore the challenges and opportunities that come with romantic relationships at this stage of life.

One of the primary challenges that individuals turning 50 may face in their romantic relationships is the fear of starting over. Many people have spent years, even decades, building a life with their partner, and the thought of starting anew can be daunting. However, it is essential to recognize that turning 50 is a milestone that offers an opportunity for personal growth and self-discovery. Embracing the challenges of starting over can lead to exciting and fulfilling romantic opportunities.

Another challenge that individuals may encounter is the changing dynamics within long-term relationships. As we age, our priorities and interests often shift, and this can create tension within a partnership. It is crucial for both partners to communicate openly and honestly about their evolving needs and desires. By doing so, they can discover new ways to navigate these changes together, ensuring the relationship continues to thrive.

Despite the challenges, turning 50 also presents numerous opportunities for romantic relationships. It is a time when individuals are more self-assured, confident, and comfortable in their own skin. This newfound sense of self can attract new partners who appreciate these qualities. Additionally, turning 50 often means having more time and freedom to invest in nurturing a relationship. Couples can embark on new adventures, travel, and explore shared hobbies, enhancing their emotional connection.

Furthermore, turning 50 allows individuals to reflect on past relationships and learn from them. This self-reflection can help identify patterns, limitations, and areas for personal growth. Armed with this knowledge, individuals can enter into new romantic relationships with a greater understanding of themselves and what they truly desire in a partner.

In conclusion, romantic relationships at the age of 50 bring both challenges and opportunities. It is essential to embrace the fear of starting over and recognize the potential for personal growth and self-discovery. Communication and flexibility are key to successfully navigating changing dynamics within long-term relationships. Turning 50 also presents exciting opportunities to attract new partners and invest in nurturing a relationship. Ultimately, this stage of life offers a chance to reflect on past experiences and enter into new relationships with a deeper understanding of oneself. By embracing the challenges and opportunities, individuals turning 50 can cultivate fulfilling and enriching romantic relationships.

Chapter 4: Career and Financial Aspects

Retirement Planning: Is It Time?

Retirement is a significant milestone in one's life, and for those who are turning 50, it is a question that often arises - is it time to start retirement planning? This subchapter aims to shed light on the importance of retirement planning, the considerations to be made, and the benefits that can be reaped by taking action sooner rather than later.

Turning 50 is a momentous occasion that brings about a mix of emotions - nostalgia for the past and anticipation for the future. However, it also serves as a wake-up call to evaluate one's financial situation and prepare for the years ahead. Retirement planning is more than just a financial process; it is a comprehensive approach to ensure a comfortable and fulfilling life after leaving the workforce.

One of the first considerations for retirement planning is assessing your current financial situation. How much have you saved? Do you have any investments? What are your sources of income? These questions will help you gauge your readiness for retirement and identify any gaps that need to be addressed. It is crucial to have a clear understanding of your financial standing before making any decisions.

In addition to financial aspects, retirement planning also involves thinking about your lifestyle goals and aspirations. What do you envision for your retired life? Are there any hobbies or passions you wish to pursue? Travel plans, volunteer work, or spending more time with loved ones are common aspirations, and planning for these activities can help ensure a fulfilling retirement.

Starting retirement planning at the age of 50 offers several advantages. Time is on your side, allowing you to make informed decisions and gradually build up your retirement savings. It also gives you the opportunity to explore various retirement options, such as downsizing your home or relocating to a retirement community, which may require careful consideration and planning.

Moreover, retirement planning at 50 allows you to take advantage of various retirement funds and investment vehicles. By leveraging tax-deferred accounts like 401(k)s or IRAs, you can potentially maximize your savings and enjoy tax benefits. It is crucial to consult with a financial advisor who specializes in retirement planning to explore the best options suited to your unique circumstances.

In conclusion, turning 50 signifies a pivotal moment in life, and retirement planning should be a priority for everyone. By assessing your financial situation, envisioning your retirement goals, and taking timely action, you can ensure a smooth transition into this new phase of life. Remember, it's never too early or too late to start planning for retirement, but the earlier you begin, the more time you have to build a solid financial foundation for the years to come.

Career Transitions and Reinvention

Subchapter: Career Transitions and Reinvention

As we approach the milestone of turning 50, many of us find ourselves reflecting on our careers and contemplating the path ahead. The truth is, career transitions and reinvention are common themes during this stage of life, yet they are often overlooked or misunderstood. In this subchapter, we will explore the realities, challenges, and opportunities that come with navigating career transitions after turning 50.

One of the most important things to realize is that making a career change at this stage is not only possible but also highly beneficial. You have accumulated a wealth of knowledge, experience, and skills throughout your professional journey, and now is the time to leverage them in new and exciting ways. Whether you are seeking a different industry, a higher position, or a complete departure from your current field, the possibilities for reinvention are endless.

However, career transitions after 50 can also come with unique challenges. It is crucial to acknowledge and address any fears or doubts that may arise. The fear of starting over, concerns about financial stability, or self-doubt about your abilities are all valid emotions. By understanding these fears, you can develop strategies to overcome them, such as seeking support from family and friends, working with a mentor, or undergoing additional training or education.

Another important aspect of career transitions is identifying your passions and interests. Take the time to reflect on what truly brings you joy and fulfillment. This self-discovery process can help guide you towards a career that aligns with your values and aspirations. Consider exploring new hobbies, volunteering, or taking up courses to explore different fields and discover hidden talents.

Networking and building connections are also crucial during a career transition. Reach out to colleagues, attend industry events, and utilize online platforms to expand your professional network. Building relationships with like-minded individuals can open doors to new opportunities and provide invaluable support and guidance along the way.

Lastly, embrace the idea of lifelong learning. The job market is constantly evolving, and staying relevant requires continuous education and skill development. Consider enrolling in workshops, online courses, or pursuing certifications to enhance your knowledge and ensure you remain competitive in your chosen field.

In conclusion, career transitions and reinvention should be seen as exciting and transformative phases of life. Embrace the possibilities that come with turning 50 and use this opportunity to explore new paths, leverage your experience, and pursue work that brings you joy and fulfillment. Remember, it is never too late to embark on a new journey and create the career of your dreams.

Financial Considerations for the Future

As we approach the milestone of turning 50, it is essential to take stock of our financial situation and plan effectively for the future. This subchapter aims to shed light on the often overlooked financial considerations that come with reaching this pivotal age. Whether you are turning 50 soon or simply want to be prepared for the future, this information is applicable to everyone.

One of the key financial considerations for those turning 50 is retirement planning. At this stage of life, retirement is no longer a distant dream but a reality that is fast approaching. It is crucial to evaluate your current retirement savings and make adjustments if necessary. Consider consulting with a financial advisor to assess your goals and develop a comprehensive retirement plan that aligns with your lifestyle and aspirations.

Another aspect to consider is healthcare. As we age, the importance of maintaining good health becomes even more evident. Health insurance coverage and plans should be reviewed to ensure they meet your changing needs. Additionally, exploring long-term care insurance options may be prudent to safeguard against unexpected medical expenses that could potentially deplete your savings.

Estate planning is another vital financial consideration for those turning 50. Updating or creating a will, establishing a power of attorney, and designating beneficiaries are critical steps to protect your assets and ensure your wishes are carried out. Estate planning also encompasses determining how you want your financial affairs to be managed in the event of incapacitation or death.

Furthermore, it is essential to reassess your investment portfolio and make any necessary adjustments. As retirement draws nearer, a more conservative investment strategy might be appropriate to protect your wealth and minimize risk. Diversifying your investments and seeking professional advice can help optimize your portfolio for long-term growth while mitigating unnecessary risks.

Lastly, financial considerations for the future should also include a review of your debt and spending habits. By reducing and managing debt, you can free up funds to allocate towards savings and investments. Evaluating your current spending patterns and identifying areas where you can cut back or save money can provide a more secure financial future.

In conclusion, turning 50 is a significant milestone that brings about unique financial considerations. Planning for retirement, reviewing healthcare coverage, estate planning, investment adjustments, managing debt, and evaluating spending habits are all crucial steps to ensure a financially stable future. By taking the time to address these considerations, you can empower yourself to make informed decisions and reap the rewards of a well-prepared financial journey.

Balancing Work and Personal Life
Subchapter: Balancing Work and Personal Life

Introduction:

Turning 50 is a significant milestone in life, a time when many people start reflecting on their achievements, priorities, and the overall balance between work and personal life. In this subchapter, we will explore the challenges and opportunities that arise as we navigate this delicate equilibrium. Whether you are an employee, an entrepreneur, a parent, or someone who simply wants to make the most of this stage, understanding how to strike a healthy balance between work and personal life will be invaluable.

Finding Harmony:

As we venture into our 50s, it becomes crucial to find harmony between our professional obligations and personal aspirations. This is a time when we may have accumulated substantial experience and expertise in our careers, but also a time when we desire more fulfillment and quality time with loved ones. Balancing work and personal life necessitates a deliberate approach, where we prioritize self-care, set boundaries, and make conscious choices that align with our values.

Reevaluating Priorities:

The truth about turning 50 is that it often brings a renewed perspective on what truly matters in life. It's essential to take stock of our goals and aspirations, identifying what brings us joy and fulfillment. Reevaluating priorities can help us make informed decisions about our careers, such as transitioning to part-time work, starting a new venture, or exploring different avenues that align better with our personal goals.

Work-Life Integration:

Rather than striving for a strict separation between work and personal life, work-life integration offers an alternative approach. By intertwining various aspects of our lives, we can achieve a more cohesive existence. This approach allows for flexibility, enabling us to attend to personal matters during work hours when necessary, and vice versa. Embracing technology and remote work options can also contribute to a better work-life integration, granting us more control over our time and reducing stress.

Creating Boundaries:

Creating boundaries is crucial when it comes to maintaining a healthy work-life balance. Learn to say "no" when necessary, delegate tasks, and establish clear communication channels to minimize interruptions. Setting aside designated time for personal commitments, hobbies, and self-care activities is equally important. By respecting these boundaries, we can prevent burnout, improve productivity, and nurture our personal relationships.

Achieving a harmonious work-life balance is an ongoing journey, particularly as we navigate the complexities of turning 50. By reevaluating our priorities, embracing work-life integration, and creating boundaries, we can enhance our overall well-being and satisfaction. Remember, finding balance is not about perfection but rather about consciously aligning our actions with our values and making intentional choices that promote both personal and professional growth.

Chapter 5: Mental and Emotional Well-being

Self-reflection and Personal Growth

In the journey of life, there comes a time when we reach a significant milestone – turning 50. It is a phase that is often surrounded by mixed emotions, unspoken fears, and societal expectations. However, what they don't tell you about turning 50 is that it can also be a time of self-reflection and personal growth.

Self-reflection is a powerful tool that allows us to pause, look within, and evaluate our lives. It is during this stage that we begin to question our choices, our accomplishments, and the direction we are heading in. Turning 50 serves as a wake-up call, reminding us that there is still time to reassess and realign our priorities.

One aspect of self-reflection at this stage is evaluating our relationships. We may find ourselves reevaluating the people we surround ourselves with and assessing whether those relationships are still serving us. It is an opportunity to let go of toxic connections and nurture the ones that bring joy and positivity into our lives.

Personal growth is another vital aspect of turning 50 that is often overlooked. This phase presents us with an opportunity to step out of our comfort zones and explore new horizons. It is a time to embark on new hobbies, learn new skills, or even pursue long-forgotten dreams.

At 50, we have accumulated a wealth of life experiences. These experiences, both positive and negative, have shaped us into the individuals we are today. Self-reflection allows us to learn from these experiences, gain wisdom, and make better choices moving forward. It is also a chance to let go of any regrets or resentments we may be holding onto and embrace forgiveness and gratitude.

Personal growth at this stage also involves taking care of our physical and mental well-being. It is crucial to prioritize self-care, adopt a healthy lifestyle, and engage in activities that promote overall wellness. This includes maintaining a balanced diet, exercising regularly, and practicing mindfulness or meditation.

In conclusion, turning 50 is not just a number; it is an opportunity for self-reflection and personal growth. It is a time to evaluate our lives, nurture meaningful relationships, and embark on new adventures. By embracing this phase with an open mind and heart, we can truly unlock the hidden potential within us and make the most of what lies ahead. So, let us embrace turning 50 as a chance to rediscover ourselves and create a fulfilling and vibrant future.

Coping with Midlife Crisis

Midlife crisis is a term that is often met with a mix of curiosity and trepidation. It is a phase that many individuals encounter as they navigate the journey of turning 50, yet it remains a topic that is rarely openly discussed. In this subchapter, we delve into the realm of midlife crisis and provide valuable insights and coping mechanisms for those who find themselves in this transformative stage of life.

First and foremost, it is important to understand that midlife crisis is a normal and natural part of the aging process. It is a period of self-reflection and introspection, where individuals may question their achievements, goals, and overall satisfaction with life. It can be a time of immense growth and personal development if approached with the right mindset.

One of the key coping mechanisms for navigating a midlife crisis is self-acceptance. Embracing the changes that come with turning 50 and accepting that life may not have turned out exactly as planned is crucial. It is essential to remember that it is never too late to make changes and pursue new passions or dreams. This is a time to reevaluate priorities and make conscious choices that align with personal values and desires.

Building a support network is also vital during this phase. Surrounding oneself with understanding friends, family, or even seeking professional help can provide the necessary guidance and encouragement. Sharing experiences and emotions with others who are going through a similar journey can be immensely comforting and reassuring.

Engaging in self-care activities is another important aspect of coping with midlife crisis. Taking care of one's physical and mental well-being becomes increasingly crucial during this phase. Regular exercise, healthy eating habits, and practicing mindfulness or meditation can help individuals find balance and navigate the emotional rollercoaster that often accompanies midlife crisis.

Lastly, embracing new experiences and challenges is a powerful way to cope with this transitional period. Trying new hobbies, pursuing further education, or even embarking on a new career path can bring a renewed sense of purpose and fulfillment. It is never too late to learn, grow, and reinvent oneself.

Midlife crisis is an inevitable part of turning 50. However, it can also be an opportunity for immense personal growth and self-discovery. By embracing self-acceptance, building a support network, engaging in self-care activities, and embracing new experiences, individuals can navigate this phase with grace and emerge stronger and more fulfilled on the other side. Remember, turning 50 is not the end; it is a new beginning.

Finding Meaning and Fulfillment

At the age of 50, many of us find ourselves standing at a crossroads, reflecting on our lives and questioning the meaning and fulfillment we have experienced thus far. This pivotal moment is often accompanied by a mix of emotions – excitement for the possibilities that lie ahead, nostalgia for the past, and perhaps even a touch of anxiety about what the future holds. In this chapter, we will delve into the truths about finding meaning and fulfillment in the second half of life, shedding light on what they don't often tell us about this transformative phase.

One of the most important realizations that often accompanies turning 50 is that true fulfillment comes from within. It is not about external achievements or societal expectations, but rather about aligning our lives with our values and passions. This is the time to take stock of what truly matters to us and make conscious choices that contribute to our sense of purpose and fulfillment.

Another truth is that finding meaning often involves letting go of what no longer serves us. As we reach midlife, we may find ourselves burdened by responsibilities, relationships, or even careers that have lost their luster. It is crucial to identify and release these burdens, creating space for new experiences and opportunities that can bring us a renewed sense of purpose and joy.

Turning 50 is also an invitation to explore new passions and interests. This is a time to step outside of our comfort zones and try things we have always wanted to do. Whether it's learning a new language, taking up a hobby, or embarking on a spiritual journey, embracing new experiences can open doors to unexpected sources of meaning and fulfillment.

Additionally, this chapter emphasizes the importance of connection and community. As we age, our relationships take on a deeper significance, and nurturing meaningful connections becomes paramount. Investing time and energy into cultivating relationships with loved ones, joining social groups, or volunteering for causes we care about can all contribute to a sense of belonging and fulfillment.

Ultimately, finding meaning and fulfillment at 50 and beyond is a personal journey, unique to each individual. It is a time for self-reflection, self-discovery, and self-acceptance. By embracing new possibilities, letting go of what no longer serves us, and nurturing relationships, we can pave the way for a fulfilling and purposeful second half of life.

In conclusion, turning 50 is not just a milestone; it is an opportunity for growth, self-discovery, and finding deeper meaning in our lives. By embracing this transformative phase with an open mind and heart, we can embark on a journey that leads us to a more fulfilling and purpose-driven existence. So, let us embrace this chapter of our lives with enthusiasm and curiosity, for the best is yet to come.

Mental Health and Seeking Professional Support

Turning 50 is a significant milestone in one's life. It can be a time of reflection, celebration, and newfound freedom. However, what they don't tell you about turning 50 is that it can also bring about various mental health challenges. It is essential to acknowledge and address these issues to ensure a fulfilling and happy life ahead.

As we age, our mental health becomes increasingly important. The demands of work, family, and personal responsibilities can take a toll on our emotional well-being. It is crucial to recognize the signs of mental health difficulties and seek professional support when necessary.

One common misconception is that mental health problems only affect a specific age group. However, mental health issues can arise at any point in life, including during the transition into your 50s. This subchapter aims to shed light on the importance of mental health and the benefits of seeking professional support.

First and foremost, it is crucial to understand that seeking help is not a sign of weakness but rather a courageous step towards self-care. Mental health professionals are trained to provide support, guidance, and tools to help individuals navigate through challenging times. They can assist in managing stress, anxiety, depression, and other mental health conditions that may arise during this period of life.

Furthermore, seeking professional support can also help individuals cope with the inevitable changes that come with turning 50. These changes may include retirement, empty-nesting, caring for aging parents, or health-related concerns. A mental health professional can offer a safe space to express concerns, fears, and uncertainties, helping individuals find resilience and adaptability in the face of these challenges.

Moreover, professional support can also play a preventive role by promoting mental well-being and resilience. Regular check-ins with a mental health professional can help individuals develop coping strategies, enhance self-awareness, and nurture positive mental habits. This proactive approach can empower individuals to make the most out of their 50s and beyond.

In conclusion, mental health should not be overlooked when turning 50. Seeking professional support is a vital component of maintaining emotional well-being and navigating the unique challenges that come with this life stage. By acknowledging the importance of mental health and taking the necessary steps to address any concerns, individuals can ensure a fulfilling and vibrant future. Remember, it is never too late to prioritize your mental health and seek the support you need.

Chapter 6: Embracing Change and New Beginnings

Pursuing Passions and Hobbies

One of the most liberating aspects of reaching the milestone of turning 50 is the newfound sense of freedom to pursue our passions and hobbies. For far too long, the demands of work, family, and other responsibilities have often taken precedence over our personal interests. However, once we cross the threshold of 50, we begin to realize that it's time to prioritize ourselves and indulge in the activities that bring us joy and fulfillment.

Contrary to what society may lead us to believe, turning 50 is not a time to slow down. It's an opportunity to embrace new experiences, explore untapped talents, and reignite the flames of our long-held passions. Whether it's painting, playing a musical instrument, writing, gardening, or even skydiving, this is our chance to pursue what truly excites us.

Often, the pursuit of passions and hobbies can have a profound impact on our overall well-being. Engaging in activities we love not only provides a break from the monotony of everyday life but also helps to reduce stress and boost our mental and emotional health. The satisfaction derived from mastering a new skill or creating something beautiful is unparalleled and can positively impact our self-esteem and confidence.

Moreover, pursuing our passions and hobbies at this stage in life can open doors to new connections and friendships. We may discover like-minded individuals who share our interests, leading to a sense of camaraderie and community. Engaging in group activities or joining clubs and organizations centered around our hobbies can provide opportunities for socialization and personal growth.

It's important to remember that age is just a number, and it should never hinder us from embracing our passions and hobbies. In fact, turning 50 can serve as a powerful reminder that life is too short to put our dreams on hold. This is the time to seize the moment and fully immerse ourselves in the activities that make us feel alive.

So, whether you've always wanted to learn to paint, try your hand at photography, or even start a small business based on your hobbies, now is the perfect time to pursue those dreams. Embrace your passions, explore new avenues, and don't be afraid to take risks. Turning 50 is an invitation to live life to the fullest and to discover the true essence of who you are.

Travel and Adventure: Broadening Horizons

In the journey of life, turning 50 is a milestone that brings about various changes and transformations. While some may perceive it as a time of slowing down and settling into a comfortable routine, the truth is that this age is a gateway to endless possibilities and new adventures. Traveling and seeking new experiences can be a powerful tool in broadening horizons and embracing the wonders that life has to offer.

As we reach the age of 50, it is common to reflect on the path we have taken and the experiences we have had. However, it is crucial to remember that there is still so much more to explore and discover. Stepping out of our comfort zones and embarking on new adventures can be incredibly rewarding, both mentally and emotionally.

Traveling allows us to break free from the monotony of everyday life and immerse ourselves in different cultures, traditions, and landscapes. It opens our minds to new perspectives, challenges our preconceived notions, and fosters personal growth. By exploring new destinations, we expand our knowledge, understanding, and appreciation of the world we live in.

Furthermore, travel offers an opportunity to reconnect with ourselves and rediscover our passions. It allows us to indulge in activities that bring us joy and fulfillment, whether it's hiking through breathtaking mountains, scuba diving in vibrant coral reefs, or simply savoring the flavors of exotic cuisines. These experiences not only bring us happiness but also help us reconnect with our inner selves, reminding us of the vibrancy and vitality that comes with turning 50.

Moreover, traveling can strengthen relationships and create lasting memories with loved ones. Whether it's a romantic getaway with a partner, an adventure-filled trip with friends, or a multi-generational family vacation, shared experiences can deepen bonds and create a sense of unity and belonging.

While the idea of travel may seem daunting or unattainable, it is important to remember that adventures come in all shapes and sizes. Exploring a nearby town, trying out a new hobby, or even taking a road trip can be as fulfilling as embarking on an international escapade. The key is to embrace the spirit of adventure and approach each experience with an open mind and heart.

So, as we turn 50, let us remember that this is not the end of our journey but rather the beginning of a new chapter filled with opportunities for growth, discovery, and adventure. Let us broaden our horizons, explore the unexplored, and embrace the wonders of travel. The world awaits us, ready to unveil its secrets and treasures.

Embracing Technology and the Digital Age

In today's rapidly advancing world, it's impossible to ignore the impact of technology and the digital age on our lives. From the way we communicate to how we access information and even how we shop, technology has revolutionized every aspect of our daily routines. As we reach the milestone of turning 50, it's crucial to understand and embrace these advancements to stay connected, informed, and relevant in this digital era.

One of the most significant benefits of technology is its ability to bridge distances and bring people closer together. With the advent of social media platforms, we can now connect and reconnect with friends and loved ones from all corners of the globe. It presents an opportunity for us, as individuals turning 50, to rediscover lost connections and build new relationships. We can share our experiences, celebrate milestones, and create a sense of community in ways that were unimaginable just a few decades ago.

Moreover, technology has opened up a vast world of knowledge and learning opportunities. Access to information has never been easier, with the internet serving as a treasure trove of knowledge. As we turn 50, it's important to embrace this wealth of information and continue to learn and grow. Online courses, webinars, and educational platforms offer endless possibilities for personal and professional development, allowing us to pursue new passions, upgrade our skills, and stay intellectually stimulated.

The digital age has also transformed the way we do business. With e-commerce booming, turning 50 doesn't mean leaving behind career aspirations or entrepreneurial dreams. Technology has leveled the playing field, providing accessibility and convenience for individuals to start their own businesses or explore new avenues. From setting up online stores to utilizing digital marketing strategies, the possibilities are endless.

However, amidst the excitement of the digital age, it's important to be mindful of its potential pitfalls. Cybersecurity and privacy concerns have become increasingly relevant in today's interconnected world. As we navigate the digital landscape, it's crucial to educate ourselves about online safety, protect our personal information, and be aware of potential scams and fraudulent activities.

In conclusion, embracing technology and the digital age is essential for everyone turning 50. It allows us to connect with others, expand our knowledge, pursue new opportunities, and stay relevant in an ever-evolving world. By adapting to the digital era, we can continue to lead fulfilling lives, achieve our goals, and remain connected to the world around us. So, let's embrace the countless possibilities that technology offers and unlock the true potential of turning 50 in the digital age.

Redefining Success and Setting New Goals

In the journey of life, turning 50 is often seen as a significant milestone. It is a time when we reflect on our achievements, our dreams, and our aspirations. However, what they don't tell you is that turning 50 is not just about looking back; it's about looking forward and redefining success.

For many, success has been defined by societal norms - a successful career, a large bank account, or material possessions. But as we reach this pivotal age, it's essential to question these conventional notions and set new goals that align with our true values and passions.

Redefining success is about finding fulfillment in all aspects of life. It's about prioritizing our health and well-being, nurturing meaningful relationships, and embracing personal growth and self-discovery. It's about finding joy in the simple things and living life on our terms.

As we enter this new chapter, it's crucial to evaluate our goals and aspirations. Have our previous ambitions brought us the happiness we expected? Are there new dreams and desires that we have yet to pursue? It's never too late to redefine success and set new goals that resonate with who we are today.

One of the keys to redefining success is to focus on what truly matters. We can shift our attention away from external validation and instead seek fulfillment from within. By aligning our goals with our values, we can create a sense of purpose and meaning in our lives.

It's also important to embrace the concept of lifelong learning. Turning 50 doesn't mean that we stop growing and developing. In fact, it's an opportunity to explore new interests, acquire new skills, and expand our horizons. By being open to new experiences and challenges, we can continue to evolve and thrive.

Moreover, redefining success means embracing self-care and prioritizing our well-being. This includes taking care of our physical, mental, and emotional health. It means finding balance in our lives and making self-care a non-negotiable part of our daily routine.

In conclusion, turning 50 is a time of reflection, but it is also an opportunity for growth and transformation. By redefining success and setting new goals that align with our true values and passions, we can find fulfillment and purpose in this new chapter of our lives. Let us not be limited by what society dictates as success, but instead, let us pave our own path and create a life that brings us true joy and contentment.

Chapter 7: The Importance of Self-care

Physical Fitness and Exercise

One of the key aspects of maintaining a healthy lifestyle, especially as we approach the milestone of turning 50, is physical fitness and exercise. While it may seem daunting to embark on a fitness journey at this stage in life, it is never too late to prioritize our well-being and reap the countless benefits that regular exercise brings.

As we age, our bodies undergo various changes, including a decrease in muscle mass, bone density, and metabolic rate. However, incorporating regular exercise into our lives can help combat these changes and promote better overall health. Exercise has been proven to boost energy levels, improve cardiovascular health, enhance mental well-being, and even slow down the aging process.

Engaging in physical activities not only helps us maintain a healthy weight but also strengthens our muscles, joints, and bones, reducing the risk of injuries and age-related conditions like osteoporosis and arthritis. Furthermore, exercise promotes better balance and flexibility, reducing the likelihood of falls and enhancing our mobility as we age.

It is important to choose exercises that suit our individual preferences, fitness levels, and health conditions. Activities such as walking, swimming, cycling, and dancing are low-impact and gentle on the joints, making them ideal choices for those just starting their fitness journey. Strength training exercises, such as lifting weights or using resistance bands, should also be incorporated to maintain muscle mass and bone density.

Before starting any exercise regimen, it is crucial to consult with a healthcare professional, especially if you have any underlying health issues. They can offer guidance and tailor a workout plan that meets your specific needs and abilities. Remember to start slowly and gradually increase the intensity and duration of your workouts to avoid overexertion or injuries.

In addition to physical exercise, it is equally important to prioritize other aspects of fitness, such as proper nutrition, sufficient sleep, and stress management. These factors work hand in hand to support our overall well-being and maximize the benefits of our exercise routine.

By making physical fitness and exercise a priority as we turn 50, we are investing in our long-term health and well-being. It is never too late to start, and the rewards are immeasurable. So lace up those sneakers, dust off that yoga mat, and join the millions of individuals who have embraced the power of exercise to age gracefully and enjoy the best years of their lives.

Nutrition and Healthy Eating Habits

Subchapter: Nutrition and Healthy Eating Habits

Introduction:

As we reach the milestone of turning 50, it becomes increasingly important to take control of our health by prioritizing nutrition and adopting healthy eating habits. In this subchapter, we will explore the truth about nutrition, debunk common myths, and provide practical tips to ensure a vibrant and fulfilling life beyond 50.

Understanding Nutrition:

Nutrition is the foundation of overall well-being, and it becomes even more vital as we age. It affects our energy levels, cognitive function, disease prevention, and longevity. By focusing on a balanced diet, we can nourish our bodies and support our health.

Debunking Myths:

There are numerous myths surrounding nutrition and healthy eating habits. Let's debunk a few of them:

1. Myth: Age requires a drastic decrease in calorie intake. Truth: While our metabolism may slow down slightly, it's essential to consume adequate calories to meet our body's energy needs. However, the focus should shift towards nutrient-dense foods.

2. Myth: Fad diets are the key to staying healthy. Truth: Instead of following restrictive diets, it's crucial to adopt a balanced approach. Include a variety of fruits, vegetables, whole grains, lean proteins, and healthy fats in your meals.

Practical Tips for Healthy Eating:

1. Emphasize Whole Foods: Opt for minimally processed foods that retain their natural nutrients. Incorporate whole grains, fresh fruits, vegetables, and lean proteins into your daily meals.

2. Portion Control: As we age, our metabolism may slow down, making portion control essential. Use smaller plates, listen to your body's hunger cues, and practice mindful eating.

3. Hydration: Staying hydrated is crucial for overall health. Aim to drink at least 8 cups of water daily and limit sugary beverages. Hydration helps maintain energy levels, supports digestion, and promotes healthy skin.

4. Meal Planning: Plan your meals in advance to ensure a well-balanced diet. This practice can help you avoid impulsive food choices and ensure that your meals contain all the necessary nutrients.

5. Mindful Indulgences: It's okay to enjoy treats occasionally, but moderation is key. Savor your indulgences mindfully, and focus on nourishing your body with nutrient-rich foods for the majority of your meals.

By prioritizing nutrition and adopting healthy eating habits, we can optimize our health and well-being beyond the age of 50. Remember to focus on whole foods, practice portion control, stay hydrated, and plan your meals wisely. By incorporating these habits into your lifestyle, you can unlock the truth about turning 50 and ensure a fulfilling and vibrant second half of life.

Sleep and Restorative Practices

One of the most underrated aspects of maintaining good health and well-being is sleep. As we age, our bodies undergo numerous changes, and the importance of quality restorative sleep becomes even more crucial. In this subchapter, we will delve into the significance of sleep for individuals turning 50, exploring various restorative practices that can help improve sleep quality and overall vitality.

Turning 50 is an exciting milestone, but it often comes with its own set of challenges. While society focuses on the physical changes that occur during this period, what they don't tell you is how crucial sleep becomes for maintaining overall health and vitality. Many individuals in this age group struggle with insomnia, restless nights, and poor sleep quality, which can lead to a myriad of other health issues.

Restorative practices provide a holistic approach to sleep, promoting not just the duration but also the quality of sleep. One such practice is establishing a regular sleep routine. Going to bed and waking up at consistent times allows our bodies to develop a natural sleep-wake cycle, enhancing the quality of sleep and ensuring a more restorative experience.

Another important aspect is creating a sleep-friendly environment. This includes keeping the bedroom cool, dark, and quiet, free from distractions that may disrupt sleep. Investing in a comfortable mattress, pillows, and bedding can also significantly improve sleep quality, reducing the risk of discomfort and restlessness during the night.

Furthermore, engaging in relaxation techniques before bed can promote a restful night's sleep. These may include activities such as meditation, deep breathing exercises, or gentle stretching routines. By calming the mind and body, these practices help reduce stress, anxiety, and tension, allowing for a more peaceful and restorative sleep.

Additionally, it is crucial to address any underlying medical conditions or medications that may be interfering with sleep. Consulting with a healthcare professional can help identify and treat conditions such as sleep apnea, restless leg syndrome, or chronic pain, ensuring a better night's sleep and overall well-being.

In

Sleep and restorative practices play a vital role in the lives of individuals turning 50. Prioritizing sleep and implementing restorative practices can lead to improved sleep quality, increased energy levels, and enhanced overall health. By recognizing the importance of sleep and taking steps to optimize rest, individuals can embrace this new phase of life with vitality and well-being. Remember, sleep is not just a luxury; it is a necessity for a fulfilling and healthy life at any age.

Mindfulness and Stress Management Techniques

In this subchapter, we will explore the powerful yet often overlooked connection between mindfulness and stress management techniques. As we navigate the uncharted waters of turning 50, it becomes increasingly important to equip ourselves with the tools necessary to maintain a healthy and balanced life. Stress is an inevitable part of life, but how we manage it can greatly impact our overall well-being.

Mindfulness, defined as the practice of being fully present and aware of our thoughts, feelings, and bodily sensations, offers a profound approach to stress management. By cultivating mindfulness, we can develop a deeper understanding of our internal landscape and learn to respond to stressors in a more constructive manner.

One mindfulness technique that can be particularly beneficial is meditation. Taking just a few minutes each day to sit in silence and focus on our breath can do wonders for our stress levels. Research has shown that regular meditation can reduce anxiety, improve cognitive function, and promote emotional resilience. It allows us to step back from the chaos of our thoughts and emotions, creating space for clarity and calmness.

Another effective technique is practicing gratitude. Turning 50 can bring about a myriad of changes and challenges, but by consciously focusing on the positive aspects of our lives, we can train our minds to shift away from stress-inducing thoughts. By cultivating gratitude, we can reframe our perspective, finding joy and contentment in even the simplest of things.

Physical activity is also a powerful stress management tool. Engaging in activities such as yoga, tai chi, or simply going for a walk can help us reconnect with our bodies and relieve tension. Regular exercise not only boosts our mood through the release of endorphins but also improves our overall physical health, which in turn can reduce stress levels.

Lastly, incorporating relaxation techniques into our daily routine can be highly beneficial. Deep breathing exercises, progressive muscle relaxation, and guided imagery are just a few examples of techniques that can help us unwind and find solace amidst the chaos of daily life.

By embracing mindfulness and stress management techniques, we can navigate the challenges of turning 50 with grace and resilience. These techniques provide us with the tools to approach stressors with a greater sense of calm and clarity, allowing us to enjoy this new phase of life to the fullest. So, take a deep breath, embrace the present moment, and embark on this transformative journey with a renewed sense of self-awareness and inner peace.

Chapter 8: Aging Gracefully and Staying Young at Heart

Cultivating a Positive Mindset

In the journey of turning 50, many people find themselves facing unexpected challenges and changes. This subchapter titled "Cultivating a Positive Mindset" aims to provide valuable insights and practical advice for individuals who are navigating the uncharted territories of their 50s. Regardless of your background or experiences, this content is dedicated to helping everyone maintain a positive mindset, enabling them to embrace this new chapter of life with enthusiasm and resilience.

As we enter our 50s, it is essential to acknowledge that life may not always go as planned. However, by cultivating a positive mindset, we can effectively adapt to these changes and find opportunities for growth and self-improvement. The first step towards achieving a positive mindset is to practice gratitude. Taking a moment each day to reflect on the things we are grateful for helps shift our focus away from negative thoughts and redirects it towards the positive aspects of our lives.

Another important aspect of cultivating a positive mindset is to surround yourself with like-minded individuals who uplift and inspire you. Building a supportive network of friends, family, or even joining social groups can provide a sense of belonging and encouragement, especially during moments of uncertainty or self-doubt.

Additionally, embracing a growth mindset is crucial when navigating the challenges of turning 50. This mindset allows us to view failures or setbacks as opportunities for learning and personal development rather than sources of disappointment. By reframing our perspectives, we can approach any obstacle with optimism and perseverance.

Practicing self-care is also a fundamental aspect of maintaining a positive mindset. Taking care of our physical, emotional, and mental well-being is crucial for overall happiness. Engaging in activities such as exercise, meditation, or pursuing hobbies that bring us joy can significantly impact our mindset and overall outlook on life.

Lastly, it is important to remember that turning 50 does not define us. Age is merely a number, and every individual has the power to shape their own future. By embracing change, maintaining a positive mindset, and actively seeking new experiences, we can make the most out of this milestone and create a fulfilling and purposeful life.

In conclusion, "Cultivating a Positive Mindset" is a subchapter that explores the importance of maintaining a positive outlook, especially when facing the challenges and changes that come with turning 50. By practicing gratitude, surrounding ourselves with supportive individuals, embracing a growth mindset, practicing self-care, and remembering that age does not define us, we can navigate this new chapter of life with confidence and optimism. This content is designed to empower and inspire individuals from all walks of life, ensuring that they have the tools and mindset necessary to embrace the truth about turning 50.

Embracing Aging with Confidence and Grace

As we approach the milestone of turning 50, many of us may find ourselves wondering about the changes that lie ahead. Society often paints a grim picture of aging, focusing on the negative aspects and limitations that come with getting older. However, in this subchapter titled "Embracing Aging with Confidence and Grace," we will explore a more positive perspective on this significant stage of life.

Turning 50 is a time of transition, and it is crucial to approach it with a sense of confidence and grace. Contrary to popular belief, aging can be a beautiful and fulfilling journey. It is an opportunity to reflect on the experiences we have had, the lessons we have learned, and the wisdom we have gained. By embracing aging with confidence, we can unlock a newfound sense of self-assurance and self-acceptance.

One of the key aspects of embracing aging is taking care of our physical and mental well-being. As we turn 50, it is essential to prioritize our health and make conscious choices that contribute to our overall wellness. This may include adopting a healthy lifestyle, engaging in regular exercise, and nourishing our bodies with nutritious foods. By doing so, we can maintain our vitality and feel confident in our bodies as we age.

Embracing aging with grace also involves accepting the changes that come with it. Our bodies may not be as youthful as they once were, but they are a testament to our journey through life. By embracing our wrinkles, gray hair, and other physical changes, we can celebrate the stories etched into our skin and hair. Each line tells a tale of resilience, laughter, and growth.

Furthermore, embracing aging with confidence and grace means embracing the opportunities that come with it. Turning 50 opens up a world of new possibilities and experiences. It is a time to reinvent oneself, explore new hobbies, and pursue passions that may have been put on hold. By embracing these opportunities, we can unleash our true potential and discover a renewed sense of purpose and fulfillment.

In conclusion, turning 50 is a significant milestone that should be celebrated and embraced. By approaching aging with confidence and grace, we can defy societal expectations and create a more positive and fulfilling experience. It is a time to prioritize our health, accept the changes that come with age, and seize the opportunities that lie ahead. So, let us embark on this journey with open hearts and minds, ready to embrace the beauty and wisdom that accompanies aging.

Maintaining a Youthful Outlook and Energy

As we approach the milestone of turning 50, it's natural to wonder what lies ahead and how we can navigate this new chapter of life. Many people might associate this age with a decline in energy and a loss of their youthful outlook. However, the truth is that turning 50 can be a time of renewed vitality and a chance to embrace new opportunities. In this subchapter, we will explore practical strategies and mindset shifts that can help us maintain a youthful outlook and energy, debunking the misconceptions surrounding this stage of life.

Firstly, it's important to remember that age is just a number. Society often imposes limitations and stereotypes on what it means to turn 50, but it doesn't define who we are or what we can achieve. Embracing a positive mindset and refusing to let age hold us back is key. By focusing on our strengths, setting new goals, and staying curious about the world around us, we can maintain a youthful spirit that transcends age.

Physical well-being also plays a crucial role in maintaining energy and vitality. Regular exercise, a balanced diet, and sufficient rest are essential components of a healthy lifestyle. Engaging in activities that we enjoy, such as dancing, hiking, or practicing yoga, not only keeps us physically fit but also boosts our mood and overall sense of well-being.

Cultivating a supportive social network is another important aspect of staying youthful. Surrounding ourselves with positive and like-minded individuals who share our passions and interests can provide a sense of belonging and foster a youthful mindset. Engaging in meaningful conversations, pursuing hobbies together, and participating in group activities can all contribute to a vibrant social life.

Furthermore, maintaining a youthful outlook requires embracing change and being open to new experiences. Trying new things, whether it's learning a new skill, traveling to unfamiliar destinations, or exploring different cultures, keeps our minds active and engaged. It's never too late to embark on a new adventure or pursue a long-held dream.

In conclusion, turning 50 doesn't have to mean a loss of vitality or a decline in our youthful outlook. By embracing a positive mindset, prioritizing our physical well-being, cultivating a supportive social network, and staying open to new experiences, we can maintain our energy and zest for life. Remember, age is just a number, and the truth about turning 50 is that it can be a time of personal growth, fulfillment, and endless possibilities.

Leaving a Lasting Legacy

As we reach the milestone of turning 50, it is natural to reflect on our lives and the impact we have made on the world. Leaving a lasting legacy becomes a priority, as we contemplate what we want to be remembered for long after we are gone. While many books and resources focus on the physical and emotional changes that come with turning 50, this chapter delves into a topic often overlooked: how to leave a meaningful and lasting legacy.

When it comes to leaving a legacy, many people immediately think of grand gestures or massive contributions. However, the truth is that a lasting legacy can be created through small acts of kindness and everyday actions. It is about the imprint we leave on the lives of others and the positive influence we have on our communities.

One way to leave a lasting legacy is through mentorship. Sharing our knowledge, skills, and experiences with those who are just starting their journey can have a profound impact. By becoming a mentor, we can empower and guide the next generation, helping them overcome obstacles and achieve their goals.

The knowledge we pass on will continue to ripple through the lives of others long after we are gone.

Another way to leave a lasting legacy is through philanthropy. Turning 50 often coincides with a period of increased financial stability and freedom. By supporting causes or organizations that align with our values, we can make a significant difference in the lives of others. Whether it is donating to education, healthcare, or environmental initiatives, our contributions can have a lasting impact on society.

Furthermore, leaving a legacy is not just about what we do for others, but also the principles and values we embody. By living a life of integrity, compassion, and authenticity, we become role models for those around us. Our actions and choices can inspire others to lead meaningful lives and make a positive difference in their own communities.

Ultimately, leaving a lasting legacy is about understanding our unique strengths and using them to make the world a better place. It is about embracing the wisdom and experience that comes with turning 50 and channeling it into something greater than ourselves. By recognizing the power we have to shape the lives of others, we can leave a legacy that will be remembered and cherished for generations to come.

In conclusion, turning 50 is a pivotal moment in our lives, and it is never too early to start thinking about the legacy we want to leave behind. Whether it is through mentorship, philanthropy, or simply living a life of integrity and compassion, we all have the ability to make a lasting impact. By embracing this chapter of our lives and using it as an opportunity to create positive change, we can leave a legacy that truly reflects the depth of our character and the mark we have made on the world.

Chapter 9: The Wisdom of Turning 50

Reflections on Life's Lessons

Life is a continuous journey filled with twists and turns, highs and lows, and an abundance of lessons to be learned along the way. As we reach the milestone of turning 50, it is only natural to reflect upon the valuable insights and wisdom that life has imparted upon us. In this subchapter, "Reflections on Life's Lessons," we dive into the profound realizations that come with this significant age, revealing what they don't tell you about turning 50.

One of the most profound lessons learned is the importance of self-acceptance and embracing who we truly are. At 50, we have spent half a century navigating through life, discovering our strengths, weaknesses, and unique qualities. It is a time to let go of self-doubt and societal expectations, and instead, celebrate our individuality and accomplishments. By accepting ourselves wholly, we can lead a more fulfilling and authentic life.

Turning 50 also teaches us the power of resilience and the ability to overcome adversity. Life has a way of throwing unexpected challenges our way, but at this age, we have gained the experience and inner strength to face these obstacles head-on. We learn that setbacks are not failures but opportunities for growth and personal development. By embracing resilience, we can rise above any setback and continue on our path with renewed determination.

Another crucial lesson that turning 50 reveals is the value of nurturing relationships. As we age, we understand the significance of genuine connections and the impact they have on our overall well-being. It is a time to cherish our loved ones, nurture friendships, and surround ourselves with positive influences. By investing in meaningful relationships, we create a support system that enriches our lives and brings us joy and fulfillment.

Lastly, turning 50 teaches us to prioritize self-care and embrace a healthy lifestyle. As we age, we realize the importance of taking care of our physical and mental well-being. This involves making conscious choices about our diet, exercise, and mental health practices. By prioritizing self-care, we can lead a vibrant and fulfilling life, ensuring we have the energy and vitality to pursue our dreams and passions.

In conclusion, "Reflections on Life's Lessons" offers a glimpse into the profound realizations that come with turning 50. It is a time of self-acceptance, resilience, nurturing relationships, and prioritizing self-care. These lessons, often unspoken, guide us towards leading a more authentic, fulfilling, and purposeful life. Embrace the wisdom that comes with turning 50 and let it be a catalyst for personal growth and happiness.

Embracing Wisdom and Experience

As we approach the milestone of turning 50, it is important to reflect on the wisdom and experience gained throughout our lives. This subchapter delves into the often unspoken truths about this significant age, shedding light on what they don't tell you about turning 50.

One of the most remarkable aspects of reaching this stage in life is the wealth of wisdom that accompanies it. By the time we turn 50, we have undoubtedly learned countless lessons from our successes and failures, relationships, and various life experiences. Embracing this wisdom allows us to navigate the challenges that lie ahead with a newfound perspective and resilience.

Turning 50 also brings a sense of liberation and self-acceptance. It is a time when we can finally shed the societal expectations and pressures that may have burdened us in our younger years. We can embrace our true selves, unapologetically embracing our quirks, flaws, and imperfections. This newfound freedom provides an opportunity to live authentically and pursue our passions without fear of judgment.

Another truth about turning 50 is the importance of prioritizing self-care and well-being. As we age, our bodies and minds require more attention and care. Investing time and effort into our health becomes non-negotiable, ensuring that we can enjoy the years ahead to their fullest. This may involve adopting healthier habits, seeking regular medical check-ups, and prioritizing mental well-being through practices such as mindfulness and self-reflection.

Furthermore, turning 50 is an opportune time to reassess our priorities and goals. It is a chance to take stock of where we are in life and make any necessary adjustments. Perhaps it's time to pursue that long-dreamed-of career change, travel to destinations we have always yearned to explore, or deepen connections with loved ones. This stage marks a perfect intersection between accumulated wisdom and newfound possibilities, allowing us to create the life we truly desire.

Ultimately, turning 50 is not just another birthday; it is a milestone that signifies a powerful transition into a new chapter of life. By embracing the wisdom and experience gained over the years, we can navigate this stage with grace and purpose. This subchapter aims to enlighten everyone who is approaching this age, assuring them that turning 50 holds the potential for growth, self-discovery, and a fulfilling future ahead.

Sharing Knowledge and Mentoring Others
Subchapter: Sharing Knowledge and Mentoring Others

As we reach the milestone of turning 50, we find ourselves in a unique position to reflect on our life experiences and the wisdom we have gained over the years. This is a time when we can choose to share our knowledge and mentor others, making a positive impact on the lives of those around us.

Sharing knowledge is a powerful way to give back to society. By imparting our insights, lessons, and expertise, we can help others navigate through the challenges and uncertainties they may face. Our experiences, both successes, and failures, can serve as valuable lessons for those who are just starting their own journeys.

Mentoring others is not limited to a specific age group or profession; it is a responsibility that can be fulfilled by anyone. Whether it's mentoring a younger colleague in the workplace, guiding a family member through a difficult decision, or volunteering to mentor a student, our expertise can be a valuable resource for others.

One of the greatest benefits of sharing knowledge and mentoring others is the sense of fulfillment and purpose it brings. As we reach the age of 50, many of us may be contemplating the legacy we want to leave behind. By taking on the role of a mentor, we can make a lasting impact on the lives of others and contribute to the betterment of society.

Mentoring also offers an opportunity for personal growth and learning. As we guide others, we are forced to reflect on our own experiences, beliefs, and values. This introspection helps us gain a deeper understanding of ourselves and enables us to continually evolve and improve.

Moreover, mentoring is a two-way street. While we may be the ones imparting knowledge and guidance, we also have much to learn from those we mentor. The fresh perspectives, innovative ideas, and enthusiasm of younger generations can invigorate our own thinking and keep us abreast of the latest trends and developments.

In conclusion, turning 50 provides us with a unique opportunity to share the knowledge and wisdom we have acquired over the years. By becoming mentors, we can make a positive impact on the lives of others, experience personal growth, and contribute to the betterment of society. Let us embrace this chapter of our lives with open hearts and minds, ready to share our knowledge and inspire those around us.

Embracing the Journey Ahead

Turning 50 is a significant milestone that often comes with mixed emotions. It's a time of reflection, a time to evaluate the journey so far and prepare for what lies ahead. In this chapter, we will explore the various aspects of turning 50 that are often overlooked or misunderstood, shedding light on the truth about this transformative phase of life.

One of the key truths about turning 50 is that it is an opportunity for growth and self-discovery. While society may portray aging as a negative process, the reality is that this is a time when many individuals truly come into their own. It's a time to embrace your authentic self, to let go of societal expectations, and to live life on your own terms. This is your chance to pursue your passions, take risks, and explore new avenues without fear or hesitation.

Another truth that often goes unspoken is the importance of self-care and well-being. As we age, it becomes crucial to prioritize our physical, mental, and emotional health. It's time to pay attention to our bodies, nurture our minds, and cultivate a positive outlook on life. This might involve adopting healthier habits, seeking therapy or counseling, or simply taking time for ourselves to relax and rejuvenate. By investing in our well-being, we can navigate the journey ahead with grace and vitality.

Turning 50 also presents us with an opportunity to redefine our relationships. It's a chance to evaluate our social circle and surround ourselves with people who uplift and inspire us. This might mean letting go of toxic friendships or reconnecting with old friends who bring joy into our lives. Additionally, it's important to nurture our relationships with family members, creating a support system that will be invaluable as we navigate the challenges and joys of this new phase.

Lastly, embracing the journey ahead means embracing change. Life is a series of transitions, and turning 50 is just another chapter in this ongoing book. By accepting change as a natural part of life, we can adapt and thrive in the face of new experiences and challenges. This might involve embracing new technologies, learning new skills, or even considering a career change. The possibilities are endless, and the journey ahead is yours to shape.

In conclusion, turning 50 is a time of transformation and self-discovery. By embracing this journey, we can unlock new opportunities for growth, prioritize our well-being, nurture meaningful relationships, and embrace change. This chapter aims to shed light on the truths about turning 50 that are often overlooked, empowering everyone to navigate this milestone with confidence, grace, and a sense of adventure.

Chapter 10: Celebrating and Embracing the Next Chapter

Embracing the Freedom and Wisdom of Age

As we reach the milestone of turning 50, we often find ourselves reflecting on our lives and contemplating what lies ahead. This subchapter delves into the liberating aspects of embracing the freedom and wisdom that come with age, shedding light on the hidden truths that nobody tells you about this remarkable journey.

One of the most treasured gifts of turning 50 is the newfound freedom that accompanies it. At this stage, many of us have raised our children, established our careers, and fulfilled numerous responsibilities. With this newfound freedom, we have the opportunity to rediscover ourselves and explore new passions and interests. Whether it's taking up a hobby we always dreamt about, traveling to unexplored destinations, or pursuing a long-held dream, turning 50 opens up a world of possibilities.

Moreover, turning 50 brings with it a wealth of wisdom gained from a lifetime of experiences. With each passing year, we have gathered valuable lessons and insights that have shaped us into the individuals we are today. This wisdom allows us to approach life's challenges and obstacles with a newfound strength and resilience. We have learned to navigate through adversity, to appreciate the simple joys in life, and to prioritize what truly matters. Our experiences have taught us to cherish relationships, nurture our mental and physical well-being, and embrace a more fulfilling and purposeful existence.

In this subchapter, we delve into the various ways we can embrace this freedom and wisdom. We explore the importance of self-care, both physically and mentally, as well as the significance of nurturing relationships and cultivating new connections. We discuss the benefits of continuing to learn and grow, advocating for the power of lifelong learning and personal development.

Furthermore, we debunk common misconceptions associated with turning 50, challenging societal stereotypes and encouraging readers to embrace this phase of life with open arms. We emphasize the potential for personal growth and fulfillment that comes with age, encouraging readers to step outside their comfort zones and embrace the opportunities that await them.

In conclusion, turning 50 is a significant milestone that brings with it a newfound sense of freedom and wisdom. By embracing this phase of life, we can unlock a world of possibilities, nurture our well-being, and continue to grow as individuals. This subchapter aims to shed light on these hidden truths, encouraging readers from all walks of life to embrace the freedom and wisdom that age brings, and to make the most of this incredible journey.

Creating a Bucket List and Pursuing Dreams

As we reach the milestone of turning 50, it's important to reflect on our lives and consider the dreams and aspirations we still hold dear. This subchapter, titled "Creating a Bucket List and Pursuing Dreams," aims to inspire everyone, especially those who are turning 50, to embrace their passions and make the most of the years ahead.

A bucket list is a compilation of experiences and goals we want to achieve before we kick the proverbial bucket. It serves as a reminder of the things that truly matter to us, igniting a sense of purpose and adventure. While turning 50 may be seen as a time of reflection, it is also an opportunity to dream big and take action.

The first step in creating a bucket list is to reflect on your values, interests, and desires. What have you always wanted to do? Where have you always wanted to go? Who do you want to become? This self-reflection will help you shape a list that aligns with your true self.

Once you have your list, it's time to start pursuing your dreams. Remember, age is just a number, and turning 50 doesn't mean you have to stop dreaming or exploring new possibilities. In fact, this is the perfect time to embark on new adventures.

Start small by checking off the simpler items on your list. It could be as simple as learning a new hobby or trying a new cuisine. As you gain confidence and momentum, move on to more significant goals like traveling to a dream destination or starting a new business venture.

However, it's crucial to keep in mind that pursuing dreams isn't just about achieving the end result. The journey itself is equally important. Embrace the challenges, setbacks, and lessons learned along the way. They will shape you into a more resilient and fulfilled individual.

Remember, you are not alone in this pursuit. Surround yourself with like-minded individuals who support and inspire you. Connect with others who are also turning 50 and share your dreams and experiences. Together, you can motivate each other to reach new heights.

In conclusion, turning 50 is an opportunity to reflect on the past, but more importantly, it's a chance to create a bucket list and pursue your dreams. Embrace the adventure that awaits, and remember that age should never be a barrier to living a fulfilling and purposeful life. Start today, and make your dreams a reality.

Finding Purpose and Making a Difference

As we approach the milestone of turning 50, many of us may find ourselves reflecting on our lives and questioning the purpose and impact we have made so far. This subchapter delves into the profound topic of finding purpose and making a difference, shedding light on the truths that they don't often tell you about this stage of life.

Turning 50 is often portrayed as a time of midlife crisis or slowing down. However, it is also an opportune moment to reassess our priorities and discover a renewed sense of purpose. It is never too late to make a difference in the world, and this chapter aims to inspire everyone to embrace this mindset.

One of the first revelations is that purpose can be found in unexpected places. While some may associate purpose with grand gestures or significant achievements, it is essential to recognize that even small actions can have a profound impact. Whether it is volunteering in your community, mentoring others, or simply being a source of support for loved ones, each act of kindness contributes to making a difference.

Another truth that often goes unspoken is that finding purpose is an ongoing journey. It is not a destination to reach but rather a continuous exploration. Turning 50 can provide the perfect opportunity to reevaluate our passions, interests, and values. By taking the time to reflect on what truly matters to us, we can align our actions with our purpose, leading to a more fulfilling and meaningful life.

Moreover, making a difference does not solely rely on external factors. It also involves personal growth and self-care. By prioritizing our well-being and personal development, we can become better equipped to positively impact the world around us. This may involve pursuing new hobbies, seeking out learning opportunities, or even embarking on a new career path that aligns with our values and passions.

Ultimately, the key message of this subchapter is that turning 50 is not the end, but rather a new beginning. It is a chance to find purpose, make a difference, and leave a lasting legacy. By embracing the truths about this stage of life, we can harness our experiences, wisdom, and passions to create a positive impact in our own lives and the lives of others.

Gratitude and Celebrating Life's Milestones

In this subchapter, we explore the importance of gratitude and celebrating life's milestones as we navigate the significant milestone of turning 50. This transitional period can be both a time of reflection and a time of anticipation for what lies ahead. It is crucial to approach this phase with a grateful heart and a willingness to celebrate the achievements and experiences that have shaped us into who we are today.

Gratitude is a powerful tool that can transform our perspectives and enhance our overall well-being. As we enter our fifties, taking a moment to acknowledge and appreciate all the blessings we have received can bring us immense joy and contentment. Gratitude enables us to shift our focus from what we lack to recognizing the abundance in our lives. By cultivating a gratitude practice, we can find peace and serenity in the present moment, which is especially valuable during this period of transition.

Celebrating life's milestones goes hand in hand with gratitude. Turning 50 is a remarkable achievement, and it is essential to honor this milestone by acknowledging the growth, wisdom, and resilience gained over the years. Whether it's throwing a party, embarking on a meaningful trip, or simply gathering loved ones for a heartfelt conversation, celebrating this milestone allows us to express gratitude for the journey we have traveled so far.

However, it's important to remember that celebrations need not be grand or extravagant. Sometimes, the most memorable moments are found in the simplest of gestures. Engaging in activities that bring us joy, such as indulging in hobbies, spending quality time with loved ones, or even pursuing new passions, can be an excellent way to celebrate turning 50.

Moreover, embracing gratitude and celebrating milestones can serve as a source of inspiration for the future. Recognizing the achievements and lessons learned can fuel our motivation to achieve even greater things in the years to come. By maintaining an attitude of gratitude and celebrating milestones, we create a positive mindset that enables us to embrace the possibilities that lie ahead.

In conclusion, the subchapter on gratitude and celebrating life's milestones sheds light on the significance of these practices as we navigate the milestone of turning 50. By cultivating gratitude and commemorating our achievements and experiences, we can find fulfillment, joy, and inspiration in this transformative period. Let us enter our fifties with a grateful heart, ready to celebrate the journey we have taken so far and eager to embrace the exciting adventures that lie ahead.

Chapter 11: THE GOOD

Life After 50: Finding Joy in the Later Chapters

While our culture tends to focus on the losses that can come with aging, there are actually many rewards found in the second half of life. With decades of experience under your belt, you can settle into a life that reflects your wisdom, passions, and sense of fulfillment. Here are some of the joys that make life after 50 so rich. More Time for Family

With career pressures easing for many as they enter their 50s, relationships with family often become a top priority. For couples whose children have left home, this is a chance to reconnect as a pair and enjoy shared interests. Grandchildren can be a major source of delight, spoiling them with attention and adventures. Some may provide childcare for working children or move closer to help aging parents, cherishing time together. With life experience to share, wisdom to impart, and family legacy to pass on, spending quality time with loved ones can be incredibly meaningful.

Financial Freedom

After years of career-building, mortgage-paying, and working toward retirement, your 50s can be when the financial pieces finally fall into place. With pensions kicking in, kids financially independent, mortgages potentially paid off, and decades of saving and investing, some will find themselves enjoying a level of financial freedom they've never had before. This unlocks opportunities for travel, hobbies, and taking on passion projects without money being such a pressing concern. There's more breathing room to consider how best to leave a legacy.

Career Growth

For those who continue working, their 50s can be the pinnacle of their career as they reach upper management, lucrative self-employment, professional influence, or long-awaited promotions. Greater confidence, poise under pressure, networking chops, and career know-how make this the prime time to earn leadership roles and mentor younger colleagues. Older professionals are deeply valued for their experience, perspective, and ability to avoid burnout. With financial stability taken care of, work can be more about meaning, fulfillment and leaving a legacy versus simply earning a paycheck.

Freedom in Daily Life

With many responsibilities of adulthood firmly under their belts, everyday life often feels freer and more flexible after 50. Most no longer have young kids or babies disrupting their schedules. Grown kids become more independent. Retirement from full-time work opens up free time. Greater financial stability provides more latitude when it comes to daily decisions. With decades of adulthood behind you, you're finally able to live a lifestyle built around your own priorities and preferences versus external obligations. There's more freedom to do as you please each day.

Focusing on Health

By your 50s, managing your health often becomes a central focus. Greater awareness of mortality as well as physical limitations that may start showing up provide motivation to double down on healthy habits. Many start exercising, eating better, reducing stress, and scheduling medical checkups. With prevention top of mind, people over 50 tend to be vigilant to any concerning symptoms and proactive about screenings. Making the most of your remaining years means being good to your body so you can stay active and energetic. Strong social ties, community engagement and spiritual practices also contribute to better mental health.

Mentoring and Giving Back

With 50+ years of experience to share, many find deep fulfillment in mentoring younger generations, whether through professional advice, volunteering, teaching, or writing. Their wisdom and counsel helps others avoid mistakes and build success faster. Leaving a positive legacy becomes more important, fueling desires to give back through philanthropy, community groups, boards, or causes. With less time left than what's already passed, contributing to the greater good provides a sense of living on through the progress made. Making a positive difference confers meaning and purpose.

Cultivating Passions

Career and family obligations often prevented people from fully cultivating their interests and passions earlier in adulthood. But life after 50 finally offers the time and freedom to dive deep. This is when people pursue dreams like launching a business, getting published, recording an album, or learning new skills. Travel for cultural enrichment, bucket-list thrills, or spiritual growth becomes a priority. There's more time to enjoy and immerse yourself in hobbies.

Creativity blossoms through mediums like painting, pottery, writing, photography and gardening. When passion projects get top billing, life feels vibrant.

Personal Growth

Life's second half is fertile ground for ongoing growth as perspectives mature and you better understand yourself. Confidence often grows from overcoming adversity, failures, losses and mistakes. A sense of purpose deepens through reflection on what matters most. Spiritual or religious faith frequently takes on new resonance later in life. Curiosity leads many to continue learning, reading voraciously across new topics and exploring fresh subjects in classes or groups. Rather than stagnating, later adulthood offers opportunities to continually expand and enrich your inner world.

Family Legacy

Leaving a meaningful legacy becomes very significant after 50. Preserving family history through photos, stories, recipes and mementos can be deeply meaningful. Passing down values, wisdom, and life lessons to children and grandchildren is a way to live on through the generations and foster their success. Providing stability and support for your family and being present at milestones confers a sense of fulfillment. Leaving financial and property legacies helps secure family prosperity. Great grandchildren allow you to see familial traits passing through the gene pool. Your legacy motivates and inspires.

Simple Pleasures

With limited time spans left, daily joyful moments gain poignancy - like morning coffee on the porch, staying up to stargaze, cooking favorite recipes, losing oneself in a craft, or sitting by a fire with loved ones. After decades of adulthood and its pressures, there's an abundance of wonder, beauty, and meaning to appreciate in the present. Noticing and slowing down to savor the small yet profound pleasures in everyday life brings great joy. With less time ahead than behind them, quiet joys are savored.

In summary, the second half of life offers plentiful sources of fulfillment through closer family ties, financial ease, career heights, lifestyle freedoms, robust health, mentoring, pursuing passions, continued growth, preserving family legacy, and appreciating simpler pleasures each day. While some deterioration is inevitable, life after 50 is about embracing and finding meaning in the remaining chapters through wisdom, purpose and joy.

Life After 50: Adjusting to the Changes

Turning 50 can be a major milestone that brings about many changes in one's life. While some may dread leaving their 40s behind, turning 50 simply means entering a new phase of life, one that is full of opportunities for growth and fulfillment. With some thoughtful adjustments, you can make the most of your 50s and beyond.

Mindset Adjustments

The first step to adjusting to life after 50 is to adopt a positive mindset about aging. Our culture tends to glorify youth and associate getting older with decline. However, 50 is still young, and with the average life expectancy rising, you likely have several decades ahead of you to enjoy. Focus on the positives - you have more life experience, wisdom and perspective now than ever before. You know yourself better and can use that self-knowledge to make choices that enrich your life. Let go of limiting beliefs about what you "should" be doing at your age. This new phase of life is yours to shape however you wish.

It's also helpful to practice gratitude for what your body and mind allow you to do. While some effects of aging are inevitable, if you've taken care of yourself, you likely have many more healthy years ahead. Appreciate your capabilities and focus less on what's declining. Adopting habits like meditation can further help train your mind to stay present and appreciate each day.

Physical Adjustments

At 50, your body may require some adjustments to stay healthy and energetic. Sticking to a regular exercise routine is essential, not just for physical health but also mental sharpness and mood. Low-impact activities like walking, swimming and yoga are ideal. Strength training helps maintain muscle mass and bone density. Listen to your body - you may need more rest days between vigorous workouts.

Nutrition is key as metabolism naturally slows down. Focus on whole, nutrient-dense foods and stay hydrated. Consult your doctor about any necessary dietary restrictions or vitamin supplements. Managing stress is also vital to limit inflammation and cortisol production, which can disrupt sleep, metabolism and immunity.

Your healthcare routine may need adjustments too. Schedule regular physical exams, cancer screenings, eye and dental exams. Get recommended vaccines and screenings. Be diligent about regular checkups, medications, and testing for health conditions more common in older adults like high blood pressure, diabetes and high cholesterol. Tracking health data through wearable devices can help you monitor trends.

Don't neglect regular skin care, including sun protection. Moisturize to combat dryness and use retinol products to encourage collagen production. Your hair will likely thin out as you age, so consult stylists about optimal haircuts, products and solutions.

Lifestyle Adjustments

This new phase of adulthood is a chance to rethink how you spend your time. Examine your priorities and interests to reflect what matters most today compared to your 30s and 40s.

Look at your career options. Do you want to stay in the same field or try something new? Adjust your workload if your current job demands are unsustainable. Seek leadership roles, mentor younger colleagues or volunteer your experience. Take on passion projects or study topics you're curious about. Many people start new careers and businesses in their 50s and beyond.

If retirement is on the horizon, develop a solid plan to ensure financial security. Review your budget and downsize if needed. Start estate planning and care for aging parents. Travel and pursue hobbies while health permits. Stay social, make new friends and try new activities. Set meaningful goals so this next phase feels purposeful, not like an end.

Relationships often need recalibration too. Communication and intimacy with your spouse may require renewed effort. Let go of friends and obligations that no longer fit. Nurture relationships that matter most. Spend time mentoring younger family members. Manage any rifts and don't let minor issues fester. Finding community and volunteering can combat loneliness and isolation.

Adapting your home environment can further support this new phase. Declutter and organize to create peaceful spaces. Make home safety updates like installing grab bars and improving lighting. Tend your living space like a sanctuary.

Mind, Body and Spirit

Focus on enriching your whole self - mind, body and spirit. Feed your mind through lifelong learning, books, podcasts, courses and cultural events. Challenge yourself mentally to strengthen cognitive skills.

Keep your spirit nourished by making time for reflection, meaning and joy. Connect with nature, explore spiritual practices, appreciate art, find flow in hobbies, and share laughter with loved ones. Look back with pride on how far you've come.

Aging well is all about balance - avoiding excess or deprivation, adapting to bodily changes, staying socially and intellectually active, aligning daily activities with purpose and meaning. Be present, peaceful and open to what this next chapter holds. With some mindset shifts and thoughtful adjustments, your 50s and beyond can be a fulfilling time to enjoy life's simpler pleasures. The key is making self-care and contentment top priorities.

Chapter 12: THE BAD

Here are 20 potential downsides of turning 50 years old:

1. Physical decline - Loss of strength, endurance, flexibility, balance, sight, hearing etc. More aches and pains.

2. Greater health risks - Higher incidence of chronic diseases like heart disease, diabetes, cancer etc.

3. Cognitive changes - Memory and recall issues, slower information processing and learning.

4. Menopause symptoms (for women) - Hot flashes, sleep troubles, mood changes.

5. Changing sleep patterns - Difficulty falling and staying asleep.

6. Weight gain - Metabolism slows down making weight loss harder.

7. Reduced career opportunities - Age discrimination in hiring, fewer advancement options.

8. Planning for retirement - Financial preparation and transitioning to new identity.

9. Caregiving duties - Caring for elderly parents and spouse's aging-related needs.

10. Loneliness - Loss of friends/family, potential isolation and depression.

11. Life regrets - Feelings of disappointment, sadness or wishing things had gone differently.

12. Fear of dying - Confronting mortality, anxiety about end of life.

13. Appearance changes - Wrinkles, grey hair, receding gums, vision needs glasses.

14. Age discrimination - Feeling devalued, patronized or ignored because of age.

15. Technology challenges - Struggling to keep up with newest innovations and platforms.

16. Changing social roles - Children grown up, new identities to adjust to.

17. Boredom and loss of purpose - Especially upon retirement, feelings of aimlessness.

18. Financial insecurity - Having inadequate savings/planning for longer life spans.

19. Decreased independence - Needing more help with daily tasks like driving, household chores.

20. Role reversals - Adult children begin managing your care and finances.

Chapter 13: THE UGLY '99'

99 Ugly issues that over fifty brings.

1. Eyesight starts to deteriorate and reading glasses become a necessity. You develop presbyopia making it difficult to focus on close objects. Reading small print in books, on medicine labels, or phone screens becomes challenging without magnification aids like eyeglasses. Even with glasses, your vision seems blurry and you find yourself holding books or menus further away to see clearly.

2. Joints and muscles lose flexibility making it harder to stay active. Your knees, hips and shoulders start to ache when going up stairs or bending down. Trying yoga poses like touching your toes feels impossible. A short jog leaves your knees sore for days. You find yourself avoiding favorite sports or physical activities you once enjoyed with ease.

3. Increased risk of chronic diseases like heart disease, diabetes, and cancer. Annual checkups reveal elevated blood pressure, glucose or cholesterol numbers that were once normal for you. You are diagnosed with type 2 diabetes, atherosclerosis, or encounter precancerous skin growths. Monitoring health issues and medications becomes part of your daily routine.

4. Skin loses elasticity leading to wrinkles and sagging. Creases on your forehead and crow's feet around your eyes become permanent fixtures. Skin on your neck sags creating jowls. Hands look more wrinkled and veins are prominent. You notice brown age spots and broken capillaries on exposed skin. Plastic surgery and injectable fillers tempt you.

5. Hair thins and grays. Your once thick mane starts to look more sparse and transparent. The spots where your scalp shows expand. Gray hairs take over to the point where regular dyeing becomes a necessity. You find hair clogging the shower drain daily.

6. Slower metabolism making it easier to gain weight. Despite consistent diet and exercise, your belly and hips expand. Losing those extra five pounds feels impossible. Clothes fit a little tighter and you go up a pant size even though you are eating less. Shedding the middle age spare tire seems like a losing battle.

7. Loss of muscle mass and bone density. Lifting heavy grocery bags leaves your arms shaky. Lower back pain from yard-work lasts for days. You find

yourself avoiding lifting heavy things. A bone density scan reveals you are at risk for osteoporosis. Standing upright gets tiring as your core strength decreases.

8. Lower energy levels and more fatigue. By 2 p.m. your motivation lags. You need a 20 minute catnap to get through the day, otherwise you fall asleep on the couch by 8 p.m. Regular daily walks wipe you out instead of energizing you. You rely on coffee to jumpstart your mornings.

9. Trouble sleeping and increased insomnia. You toss and turn before falling asleep. Multiple bathroom trips disrupt your sleep cycle all night. Early morning wake ups start your day feeling exhausted. OTC sleep aids become your nightly ritual. You start dozing off watching TV in the evening.

10. Loss of hearing, especially high frequency sounds. Your family complains you play the TV too loudly. You ask people to repeat themselves and have trouble understanding conversations in noisy places. Ringing phones, smoke alarms, and doorbells don't register unless they are right next to you. You avoid social settings that would require focused listening.

11. Weaker immune system and longer recovery from illnesses. Colds last for weeks instead of days forcing you to cancel plans. Vaccines like the flu shot make you feel low energy. Minor cuts and scratches are slow to heal. A shingles outbreak keeps you home in misery for over a month. You become more paranoid about germs, sanitizing frequently.

12. Loss of height as spine compresses. Your driver's license needs to be updated to a lower height. Standing tall and upright starts to hurt your back. Always looking a bit downward causes neck soreness. You joke about being part of the shrinking population.

13. Less efficient oxygen uptake during exercise. A flight of stairs leaves you winded. Long walks require multiple rest breaks. Once simple yard chores now require pacing yourself. Breathing hard lifting groceries alarms you. Gym workouts need to be modified as your endurance declines.

14. Decreased balance and coordination raising fall risks. A misjudged curb nearly causes you to fall. Knees and ankles seem to twist more easily on uneven ground. Getting up quickly makes you lightheaded. You take the elevator more to avoid tripping while climbing stairs. Fear of falling keeps you from activities requiring coordination like dancing, biking or hiking on rocky trails.

15. Forgetfulness and reduced mental sharpness. You misplace your glasses, wallet and keys daily. Recalling coworkers' names from years back becomes

impossible. You forget entire conversations by the next day. Keeping track of plots and characters when reading gets tricky. You depend more on calendars, to do lists and reminders to jog your fuzzy memory.

16. Slower reflexes and reaction time. Getting startled by sounds is a regular occurrence since your reactions are slower. Scrambling to find the ringing phone takes longer. You find yourself doing a double take checking for traffic before crossing streets. Catching keys fumbled from your hand is hit or miss.

17. Low libido and sexual dysfunction. Intimacy drops lower on your priority list. Erectile problems require medications like Viagra. Vaginal dryness makes intercourse uncomfortable sans lubricants. Orgasms take more effort and seem less intense. Your sex drive and performance decline despite a willing partner.

18. Urinary incontinence. When you laugh, sneeze or cough, a bit of pee leaks out unexpectedly. Chores like mopping the floor can cause embarrassing leaks. You wear panty liners and keep extra underwear on hand. Planning outings requires knowing all the bathroom locations in advance.

19. Digestive issues like GERD, constipation and bloating. Acid reflux keeps you up at night requiring antacids and sleep wedges. Fiber supplements and stool softeners become essential to stay regular. Your stomach looks distended and feels tender to the touch after eating even small portions. Bowel urgency gives you little warning.

20. Higher cholesterol levels. Despite limiting red meat, cholesterol numbers creep up year after year. Blood tests reveal high triglycerides and LDL and low HDL. Your doctor prescribes daily statins to protect against atherosclerosis and heart attacks. Dietary restrictions grow as you monitor fat intake obsessively.

21. Hormonal changes for menopause in women. Hot flashes disrupt your work making layers of clothing necessary year round. Heavy irregular periods bring cramps, anemia and embarrassment. Vaginal dryness causes painful intercourse. Mood swings and irritability isolate you socially. Sleep disturbances add to severe fatigue.

22. Prostate issues in men. Nightly bathroom trips interrupt sleep. A weak stream takes patience. Leaking after urinating requires extra clean up. Medications manage increased prostate volume, infections and incontinence. nerves about prostate cancer lead to annual screenings.

23. Dental and gum problems. Even with diligent brushing, your dentist notices more cavities and gum recession. A tooth implant replaces a molar lost to cracking. The high costs of dental work on limited insurance is a hardship. More frequent cleanings try to ward off expensive issues.

24. Foot and ankle swelling. Your shoes start to pinch your feet mid day. Taking off your socks reveals indentations and puffiness. Veins protrude on top of feet and ankles. Elevating your legs when sitting provides relief from the pooling fluids. Shoes in a larger size are always reserved in your closet for high puff days.

25. Increased sensitivity to temperature extremes. Winters require bundling up in layers even indoors. Summers cause you to overheat, turn red and sweat faster than in your youth. Keeping comfortable at work, home and socially means frequently removing layers or blasting the A/C. Your thermostat gets a real workout as your internal thermometer seems off.

26. Loss of sense of smell. Foods seem bland needing extra spice. Eating becomes more about nutrition than flavor. You can't smell smoke from burning food in the kitchen. Body odor and bad breath goes unnoticed prompting others to discreetly tell you. The scent of flowers and clean laundry no longer register like they once did.

27. Bruising more easily from thinner skin. Your legs are mottled with random bruises from merely bumping into tables and chairs. Minor scrapes cause ugly bruising lasting weeks. You notice purplish skin under your arms when changing shirts. Using heating pads risks ugly marks. You strangely find yourself comparing bruise colors and patterns with friends.

28. Cellulite becomes more stubborn. The back of your thighs and your buttocks look dimply and rippled no matter how toned the muscles are. Aerobics classes and squats seem useless against puckering skin. Your basic black swimsuit requires a cover up. The smooth summer legs of your youth are a distant memory.

29. Nails become brittle and yellow. Your nicely manicured nails develop ridges and start peeling. Polish seems to chip next day. Toenails thicken with fungus no matter the pedicures. Keeping nails trimmed is key to preventing painful splits and tears. Cuticles never stay neatly pushed back. The weekly chore of filing and buffing grows tiresome.

30. Varicose veins appear. Ropey purple veins bulge noticeably on your legs. They worsen and spread with age, pregnancy and inactivity. Veins around your ankles multiply after decades of standing. Some tender veins may require surgical removal when severe. Aging and genetics seem unavoidable culprits despite weight and diet. You reminisce about the vein free legs of youth.

31. Joint and back pains. Your knees creak audibly when climbing out of cars. Stiff fingers and toes ache moving them in the morning. Your lower back tightens up when standing to cook or wash dishes. Daily stretching provides minimal relief from chronic stiffness. Anti-inflammatories seem part of your daily regimen. You feel envy seeing seniors still running marathons.

32. Insomnia and trouble sleeping through the night. Staring at the clock from 2 a.m. onwards is routine. Tossing, turning and punching pillows nightly fails to bring sound sleep. Stress weighs on you consciously and unconsciously. Falling asleep yet waking up exhausted becomes the norm with only brief intervals of restful sleep. You start to dread the frustration of going to bed.

33. Anxiety and depression become more common. Losses and changes associated with aging frequently trigger bouts of worrying and sadness. Fears about death or developing dementia amplify with time. Emotional issues can lead to withdrawal and melancholy if not managed. Counseling, medications, exercise and companion animals provide mood relief and coping skills.

34. Loneliness from retirement or children moving away. Days alone stretch out aimlessly with more time on your hands after retirement. Kids busy with their own families only visit on occasion. In person social interaction decreases leaving you isolated. Pursuing hobbies or being active helps counteract the stillness after years of a busy household.

35. Career stagnation as ambitions wane. Getting passed over for promotions you once coveted barely phases you now. You feel less driven to learn new skills or technologies needed for advancement. Colleagues your junior move to higher positions while you coast to retirement. Shifting priorities away from career is a welcome relief and release.

36. Social isolation and less community immersion. Your social landscape narrows to a few close friends as you age. Keeping up with friends moves online rather than in person. Hobbies that connected you to groups fade away. Professionally you shift to consulting roles versus collaborative projects. Outside of family, your world grows smaller and more insular.

37. Declining cognitive skills like multitasking and focus. You leave the stove on forgetting finished cooking. Following complex plots in books or movies feels exhausting. Learning new computer programs requires tech savvy grandkids' help. Staying focused during long meetings or tasks becomes truly challenging for your scatterbrain.

38. Less engagement and willingness to try new things. Your motivation to sample exotic new cuisines or travel to far flung locations dwindles. Tending your garden or watching TV keeps you content and occupied. Visiting new places seems more hassle than adventure. Sticking to comfortable routines trumps the effort needed to learn and explore.

39. Negative biases harden and openness decreases. You find yourself being more judgmental about societal changes or issues like politics, gender roles, and civil rights. The beliefs and world views you've held rigidly for decades seem unchangeable now. Adapting your perspectives to accommodate new realities feels threatening. You risk being left behind.

40. Financial planning becomes more challenging. Stretching your retirement accounts to cover multiplying medical bills and basic living expenses keeps you anxious. Unexpected costs like car repairs carry heavy consequences. Losing your spouse requires major financial revisions. Rising taxes and inflation strain budgets built for a different era.

41. Coming to terms with mortality. Aches, forgetfulness and declining abilities are constant reminders of aging. Thoughts of final decline and death start to weigh on you. But the wisdom of years also grants perspective on what matters most in life. Making meaning of your legacy becomes more crucial.

42. Change or loss of identity and purpose. You feel a bit lost and aimless after your kids leave home and daily work grind ends. Roles that long defined you abruptly shift leaving you searching for new meaning and identity. Finding challenging but gratifying activities helps you rediscover a sense of purpose.

43. Letting go of youthful looks and vitality is difficult. Your daily reflection reveals undeniable aging including wrinkles and graying hair. Vanity over appearances may fade, but mourning the vitality of youth persists. Early rising for fitness, reasonable diets and smart beauty routines help you make peace with changes.

44. Fear of irrelevance or obsolescence. Rapidly advancing technology intimidates you, making communication with grandkids who are "digital

natives" frustrating. Your career skills and institutional knowledge seem antiquated amid younger rising staff. You work to stay useful through up skilling, consulting, teaching, volunteering or mentoring.

45. Loss of loved ones and coming to terms with death. Losing a spouse, siblings or close friends increasingly becomes part of life. Support groups and grief counseling help cope with mounting loss. The reality of dying starts to sink in as your age cohort declines. You consciously appreciate time with loved ones here and now.

46. Regret over past decisions and missed opportunities. Looking back, forks in your road elicit sadness over paths not taken in relationships, careers, family and finances. But practicing self-forgiveness and moving forward mindfully allows peace. The roads you did take got you to the now.

47. Feelings of bitterness or dissatisfaction with life. Pain, irreversible changes and imposed limitations breed resentment as the carefree days of youth recede. An attitude of gratitude and focusing energy on what you can do and control helps thwart unchecked bitterness. Tomorrow carries potential.

48. Fear of burdening others due to declining health. Relying on family or friends when you're ill or physically weak feels uncomfortable. Open communication ensures your needs are heard so caregivers provide support willingly without strain. There may come a time when you can reciprocate.

49. Concerns over who will handle future caregiving. Thoughts of needing comprehensive daily assistance worry you, especially if you live alone. Researching appropriate housing, services and financial options eases fears about maintaining health and independence as long as possible.

50. Anxiety over running out of time to accomplish goals. Once elusive dreams like traveling, writing a book or relearning piano now seem possible with time flexibility. But worries surface on whether your health and faculties will permit achieving them. Prioritizing the most meaningful goals motivates you to pursue them sooner than later.

51. Age discrimination at work makes you feel undervalued. Despite extensive experience, younger hiring managers overlook you. Your deep expertise gets discounted. Feeling marginalized and unappreciated takes a toll.

52. Friends only want to talk about health issues. Conversations become less fun and shift to comparing ailments or latest treatments. Reminiscing about the past seems more enjoyable than talking about the present.

53. You are viewed as technologically incompetent. People assume you don't know how to use computers, smart phones, apps and digital services. In reality you're more tech savvy than given credit for.

54. Pop culture references go over your head. When young people reference movies, slang, memes or trends you're at a total loss. The entertainment and icons that defined your generation feel forgotten.

55. Things that used to be easy now require effort. From household chores to socializing, activities that once came simple require rest breaks, better tools, reading glasses or preparation to enjoy.

56. Fewer networking opportunities stall career growth. In an era of digital profiles and influencer branding, professional networking happens less through conferences or community events that played to your strengths.

57. Sacrificing spontaneity for health needs. Making plans requires considering access to bathrooms, comfortable shoes, available snacks, and energy levels. Spontaneity yields to practicality.

58. Being dismissed as cranky or grumpy unfairly. Expressing seasoned opinions gets written off as complaining versus the wisdom that comes with experience. You have to laugh off the "old curmudgeon" comments.

59. Reading fine print is impossible without magnifiers. Detail oriented tasks like reading contracts, assembly instructions and work documents become arduous. Font choice matters more now.

60. Everyone else seems loud while your hearing weakens. Conversing in noisy restaurants or crowded rooms gets tiring as voices blur into loud background noise. Lip reading helps fill in the muffled gaps.

61. Your taste in music seems dated. The pop songs and bands you listened to in high school and college are deemed classics. Music made after the 90s sounds like noise.

62. Disheartened to see favorite places disappear. With every store, restaurant, or building from your youth that vanishes, a little history feels lost. But progress demands change.

63. Fewer clothing options flatter an aging body. Even with time and money, finding flattering clothing that aligns with your personal style requires patience and tailoring.

64. Things you once easily memorized now escape you. Recalling songs, movie lines, poetry excerpts, or Bible verses you've known for decades suddenly seems challenging. Time erases what was once second nature.

65. Daily multivitamins become essential routines. Your physician emphasizes supplements to fill nutritional gaps that diet alone can no longer provide adequately.

66. Your drink preferences shift to wine and spirits over beer. A nightly cocktail appeals more than a six pack. Taste buds evolve but drinking responsibly remains important. Moderation matters more.

67. Being called Sir, Ma'am or, gasp, Grandma/Grandpa. Honorifics denoting respect still manage to make you feel aged. But they do beat the alternative of appearing even older.

68. Fewer dating options for divorced or widowed singles. If reentering the dating world, traditional ways of meeting like-minded prospects dwindle. Odds feel stacked against finding companionship.

69. Wishing your dismayed doctor good luck finding veins. Hydrating well before blood draws becomes necessary as your veins get more difficult to locate. You thank phlebotomists profusely for their patience and skill.

70. Clothes shopping requires higher necklines and longer hemlines. Preserving modesty and highlighting assets dictates more conservative choices than in decades past. But elegance trumps everything.

71. Your idea of adventure travel is now a nice hotel. Roughing it loses appeal as creature comforts provide needed recovery from full activity days. You happily embrace being a "glamper" versus camper.

72. Choosing between mental acuity and physical stamina. Exercising your body helps it stay resilient but leaves you more fatigued. Exercising your mind keeps you sharp but less fit. Finding balance between the two is hard.

73. Coming to terms with an estranged family before it's too late. You reach out to rebuild severed ties with siblings, children or parents as years go by. Time together matters more than old differences now.

74. Fewer career opportunities lead to resume gaps. Your niche disappears so reentering the workforce means gaps between jobs or starting over in new fields. Explaining lapses requires finesse.

75. Things shift from how long you lived somewhere to how long you lived. Swapping stories, you realize it's less about where you've been than how long you were present somewhere. Perspective shifts.

76. Doctors look way too young. Seeing physicians fresh out of medical school makes you miss the veteran doctors who treated you for decades prior and knew your whole health history. It takes time to build trust with new docs.

77. You are annoyed by loud teenagers in public. Patience wears thin for boisterous, noisy youth in restaurants and stores. Their rowdiness offends you more than it once did years ago when you related better.

78. Your brain starts playing tricks making you doubt reality. Occasional memory glitches leave you wondering if events really happened or if your mind is playing tricks. Note taking becomes more crucial.

79. Acronyms and shorthand make conversations confusing. From texting terms to workplace jargon, you find popular abbreviated words uttered in conversation totally indecipherable.

80. Trouble differentiating faces and names of younger celebrities. The meteoric churn of new actors, musicians and stars fast forward pop culture leaving you clueless. Google becomes essential to figuring out who's who.

81. Jokes about your age are funny but hit close to home. The age related punchlines you crack make everyone laugh, while also reinforcing how old you've become. Comedy with a price.

82. Knowing your lifelong friends better than family. Friends with decades of shared history together understand you better than newer in law family members who entered your life later on. Bonds deepen through time.

83. Feeling socially excluded by cultural references. Not knowing details like Hogwarts Houses or TikTok memes makes you feel left out of popular culture conversations. It's increasingly alien territory.

84. Tension between aging parents and adult children. Roles flip as parents rely more on kids for caregiving and financial help. Relinquishing independence is challenging on both sides.

85. Coming to terms with biggest regrets and sorrows. Making peace with painful mistakes, losses and "if onlys" is crucial to avoid fixating on woulds, could or should haves at life's end.

86. Boredom from lack of challenges or drives. Retirement can lose meaning without engaging projects or volunteering. Finding new goals and problems to solve wards off restlessness.

87. Failing memory means repeating stories. Forgetting what details you shared already leads to retelling the same stories or anecdotes to friends who gently nod along.

88. Dealing with hurricane, earthquake and lockdown prepping. From emergency supplies to contingency plans, later life now involves preparing for natural disasters, pandemics and other disruptions.

89. Surrendering car keys due to declining vision or reflexes. The loss of independence from giving up driving due to safety reasons takes an emotional toll. But preventing accidents is critical.

90. Adjusting to children being busy with grandchildren. Your kids devote energy to raising their kids, limiting time for you. Though bittersweet, cherishing the new generation bonding with them is rewarding.

91. Coming to terms with stuff accumulation. Years of acquiring possessions now requires paring down. This means parting with belongings full of memories, but also liberating.

92. Fearing you'll be a burden on loved ones some day. Needing serious future caregiving weighs on you. Having open dialogue with family about wishes and contingencies provides reassurance.

93. Worrying about healthcare costs as health declines. Even with insurance, medical costs drain finances fast. Long term care planning eases fears about managing expenses as needs multiply.

94 Feeling irrelevant as generations shift workplace roles. Your successor or mentor roles fade as younger Gen X or Millennials take over management and training. Passing the baton graciously takes maturity.

95. Missing how things used to be but accepting change. Nostalgia creeps in for the lost days of your youth and young adulthood. But change is inevitable and each season has its own rewards.

96. Coming to grips with never realizing once-held dreams. Recognizing hopes that will go unfulfilled like acting, traveling abroad or starting a company requires realistic perspective. Some visions remain fantasies.

97. Making new friends gets harder. Finding compatible new friends beyond existing circles is challenging. Pursuing common interests, classes and hobbies helps meet like-minded acquaintances.

98. Fewer milestone ages feel exciting. Hitting 60, 70 or 80 doesn't have the thrill that 30, 40 or 50 carried. But this frees you to define major milestones on your own terms.

99. Greater anxiety about the health of the remaining parent(s). Losing one parent is hard. Worrying about the surviving parent's health and independence intensifies as their support system and caregiver declines.

Closing Summary

Despite the myriad challenges - aches, pains, loss of vitality, cognitive decline - accepting aging as a natural part of existence is key to facing our later years with poise, wisdom and gratitude. When we stop fighting vainly against this inexorable biological process, we can direct energy toward making the most of the years we have left. We appreciate the remarkable journey behind us, become motivated to realize deferred dreams, and adopt an age-positive mindset that dims the sting of discrimination. Acknowledging aging's inevitability inspires reflection on purpose and legacy. Expecting new limitations as part of life's cycles fosters adaptation and resilience. The right philosophical perspective helps us gain peace with giving up youth and control as we follow nature's path. Though growing older brings difficulties at every turn, embracing aging as a natural progression instills courage to engage fully in the present moment - the only time we can live.

Milton Keynes UK
Ingram Content Group UK Ltd.
UKHW020640261023
431376UK00016B/598